THE GOD OF NO GOOD

THE GOD OF NO GOOD

SITA WALKER

ultimo
press

Published in 2023 by Ultimo Press,
an imprint of Hardie Grant Publishing

Ultimo Press
Gadigal Country
7, 45 Jones Street
Ultimo, NSW 2007
ultimopress.com.au

Ultimo Press (London)
5th & 6th Floors
52–54 Southwark Street
London SE1 1UN

  ultimopress

 A catalogue record for this book is available from the National Library of Australia

The God of No Good
ISBN 978 1 76115 131 6 (paperback)

Cover design Alissa Dinallo
Author photo Courtesy of Natalie McKain
Text design Simon Paterson, Bookhouse
Typesetting Bookhouse, Sydney | 11.75/18.5 pt ITC New Baskerville
Copyeditor Elena Gomez
Proofreader Pamela Dunne

10 9 8 7 6 5 4 3 2 1

Printed in Australia by Griffin Press, an Accredited ISO AS/NZS 14001 Environmental Management System printer.

Ultimo Press acknowledges the Traditional Owners of the Country on which we work, the Gadigal People of the Eora Nation and the Wurundjeri People of the Kulin Nation, and recognises their continuing connection to the land, waters and culture. We pay our respects to their Elders past and present.

For my daughter, and my sons.

2011. Brisbane.

I am in a coffee shop slash book store in Stones Corner when my husband tells me he doesn't want to be married to me anymore. We are drinking cafe lattes and I have just taken a bite out of a vanilla custard slice. There is icing sugar on my face.

This would not be surprising if we had been fighting or arguing, but since we had just decided to go out for a coffee on a Sunday morning because his mother was free to look after the kids, to somewhere as innocuous as Stones Corner, I'm fairly taken aback by the presentation of divorce papers. It feels like going on a cruise and being told, 'Actually, you're being deported. I hope you've packed everything you own.' I stifle a giggle and wipe the icing sugar from my lips.

Oh. He's serious.

We didn't get divorced that Sunday morning. We didn't even get divorced the next time Borhan pulled out the papers. We waited until we were fifteen years in, with three small children, which is of course the ideal time to split up. Fortunately, this was not the first relationship of mine that had ended. I'd already experienced a much more traumatic break-up in the years leading up to this moment – I'd left God.

To be fair, Borhan left God first. He left God like Noel Gallagher left Oasis. He peeled religion off like a pair of too-tight jeans and tossed it away. He boldly announced to me, his family, his community and his children that he had lost his faith.

Leaving one's religion shockingly and publicly isn't the sort of thing that most people who have been brought up in intensely faithful homes do, though in hindsight it seems on brand for Borhan. I should have seen the yellow envelope, and the latte, coming.

This is not a book about divorce. It's not a book about God, either. You might think it is a book about goodness and what it means to be a good person, but it isn't. Like everything else, this is about love.

When I left God, I had nothing of Borhan's certitude or courage. My break-up with the Almighty was more like a French exit. I stealthily took tiny pieces of God out of my life, one by one, under cover of darkness. And nobody – not even God – noticed I was gone.

Well, not nobody.

Nine months ago.

I slip a cigarette and a lighter into my pocket and sneak out the front gate, into the cul-de-sac. I make my way into the grassy laneway that leads to the bus stop, and walk halfway down it before lighting up and taking a deep drag. Tarragindi, the treed suburb where we live on the south side of Brisbane, is blooming and ripe with the promise of summer. There has been so much November rain that the air is beginning to hold water underneath its skin. The grass in the lane is lush and thick under my feet, and the fence of the yard running parallel is overflowing with passionfruit vines and grapevines and leafy shrubs. Behind the fence a few chooks are scratching about. City chooks, pecking at bok choy stumps and multigrain bread and teabags. They don't flutter when I pass.

The house at the end of the lane is a two-storey cement and chrome box, with glass surrounding the pool and a postmodern marble statue devoid of imagination in the entranceway. It's the type of place where a man in a Ralph Lauren shirt slaps his wife around and cries about it later, buying her bottles of Veuve Clicquot to make up for her bruises. The next day they call each other 'baby' and eat muesli and fat-free yoghurt for breakfast and she takes the day off work. Their kids go to a Catholic primary school, but they've never been to church. He never means to hurt her. Doesn't he show her how much he loves her with everything he gives her? This house? The yard and cars? The magnolia tree he planted for her against the fence?

It's an enormous tree. As beautiful as the house is ugly. It spills over into the lane, trying to escape. With the dart dangling from my lips I reach up and pull down a large branch. I pluck the most extraordinary magnolia bloom from the tree and inhale its thick perfume. The scent gives me an urge to sit down in the grass with my flower and my cigarettes and take my shoes off. But that would be weird, so I walk slowly back down the lane, taking gentle drags, watching to make sure the kids haven't suddenly decided to ride their bikes down the lane. From the chook and vine house on my right I hear some gentle rustling, and a gentleman emerges, secateurs in hand.

'Hi,' I say, surprised. 'Sorry about the smoke. I'm just hiding from my kids.'

'It's no problem.' He smiles.

He's tall and imposing, with a large moustache. He looks about seventy-five, but could be older. He has a weather-worn, intelligent face and a t-shirt that says 'From Little Things Big Things Grow'. Something in his demeanour makes me think he's European. An elegance, perhaps. He looks like Stalin.

'My kids think one cigarette will kill me. They're very judgemental about smoking.'

'Well, that's human nature. To judge.'

Definitely European. A slight accent gives it away.

'I suppose so,' I nod.

'Forget about it and have another. I don't mind.' He nods towards the bloom in my hand. 'You want to steal one of my flowers too?'

'Yes, I'd love that,' I say, grinning. It feels like I've known him for a long time. He cuts a delicate pink flower from a shrub at his feet, and a few orange marigolds from another. 'You live down the lane?' he asks, and passes the flowers over the fence.

'Yes, I live next door to Peter and Judy.'

'You're the girl with the Indian name?'

Ever since I started school I've been 'the girl with the Indian name'. It's because I don't look brown. I look white. Some people think I'm Spanish, or Greek. My mother isn't actually Indian, but she isn't really Iranian either. She's Parsi. They're a hybrid, country-less race of people who nobody in Australia has ever heard of. Zoroastrians who fled Iran in the eighth century to avoid religious persecution. They set sail for India and have been there ever since, marrying Indians and other Iranians, and each other. Mostly I tell people 'my mother grew up in India' which could imply that she was either the daughter of the British Raj or a chai walla from Calcutta. Either way, it usually ends the questioning.

'Yes, it's "Sita". My mother grew up in India.'

'I'm Joseph, Sita. Nice to meet you. Is your mother Indian?'

'No, she's Parsi.'

'Oh, so you're Zoroastrian?'

My eyebrows raise themselves involuntarily. 'No, actually. My mother is a Bahá'í . . . it's a relig–'

'I know what it is. Bahá'ís believe in one god. Unity of religions, yes?'

'That's the one, yep.' I'm taken aback.

'Are you a Bahá'í?' he asks, genuinely interested, pruning the mock orange.

'I'm not sure what I am.'

He gives a gentle chuckle.

'Thank you for these. They're lovely,' I say by way of exit, stubbing my dart on a steel fence post and turning to leave with my marigolds.

'You must be in love, yes, Sita?'

I turn back in surprise, wondering if I've heard correctly. Even more astonishing is the answer that falls out of my mouth: 'I think I might be.'

'Ah.' He shakes his head. 'Nobody thinks they're in love. You're either in love or you're not in love.'

Maybe he's German. The way he says 'love' sounds a little bit like 'luff'. The way he's questioning me is definitely Germanic.

'I am in luff, Joseph.' I say, with a resignation the statement doesn't really deserve.

He nods and overturns a restaurant-grade mayonnaise bucket filled with weeds, lowering himself down slowly, in the way of tall older men who are still fit but just a little swollen in the joints. I offer him a cigarette through the wire fence and take another one myself, sitting down cross-legged in the grassy laneway.

'So. What's the problem then?' he asks, slipping the dart between his lips and cupping the lighter flame with a brown leafy hand.

'What is it about me that makes you think I'm in love?'

'I know you don't have a husband, because Judy told me and Rupi, when she came over to play cards last week. And I've never seen you smoking in the lane before, so something is making you feel stressed or nervous. Excited perhaps? But mostly it's the way you're holding the flowers. Like a lover would.'

I laugh at this absurd detective work. Mostly because of its accuracy.

'Perhaps I just like flowers?' I reply.

'What's the problem with being in love?' He persists, like a border collie with a tennis ball.

'I don't want to be in love, Joseph!' I say, sassing him just a bit, this old man I've never met. He likes it. When I'm old, I hope young men sass me while I'm pruning my roses. He grins, surrendering. We sit in companionable silence for a few minutes. Joseph finishes his smoke, puts it out in the grass, stands up with a little groan and lays the butt neatly on the mayonnaise bucket. Picking up the secateurs, he rubs his elbow and announces, impressed: 'I've never met a girl who didn't want to be in love.'

'I'm too old to be a girl,' I say. Mona Lisa smile.

I can't resist a man who is impressed by me, even if he is older than God. I love male approval. It's one of my worst qualities.

He deftly pulls some stray leaves and twigs from the hedge and tosses them on the pile of weeds. 'You're playing hide and seek in a laneway and stealing flowers, yes?' he says with a smile. 'You look like a girl to me.'

I stand up and brush myself off, laughing.

'I haven't fallen in love for a long time,' he says, pruning the grapevine now. 'I love my wife. We have been married forty years. It's a different love now. I don't think I can remember what it was like to fall in love.'

I think of the way it felt to hold him while he wept. The way I wake up and want to do something for him. Anything. To worry about him, to urge him to eat more greens, to reach over in the dark in the middle of the night and feel his chest rise and fall. I think about how he sends me novels to read, and play after play – Miller, Stoppard, Williams, Cristofer. He's dug a moat around me and now he's filling it with words, protecting me with the only shield he has – stories. A river of love and pain and bliss and pride and sorrow and mercy and courage and laughter and wisdom and bold vengeance and surprising hate. I think of how loving him makes me want to be his slave and his ruler both at once. How I see him as a boy and as a man, one inside the other like a Russian doll, and I am the same – a girl and a woman at once in his arms.

I think of how I don't want any of it.

Love and pain are two fangs of the same snake. You cannot be pierced by one without also being poisoned by the other. This is why the fearful can never truly love. They can't bear the pain.

I look at Joseph and smile gently. 'Anyone can fall in love, but not everyone can stay in love. Forty years is a long time. I'm sure you and Rupi know love better than I do.'

1989. Toowoomba.

I'm eight years old and every night I pray for God to make me good. I want so desperately to be good. My mother, Fari, is big on 'good'. She is not interested in whether I can read or write, whether I know how to dance or how to cook, or how to play the piano. She is interested in whether or not I am on good terms with the Almighty.

Do I pray every morning and every night? Do I bring myself to account each day? Am I kind? Do I treat others how I would like to be treated? Fari is always saying, 'You must be kind to all people and love them with a pure spirit. To live the life is to be no cause of grief to anyone.'

I fear I cause daily grief to many. I dabble in a variety of sins, the least of which is my sharp tongue. To wit, Fari likes to gently remind me that we should 'never allow ourselves to speak one unkind word about another – even though that other be our enemy'. Good people don't backbite or gossip, and they always tell the truth.

Just this week I called one of the neighbourhood kids a 'pig-bird' behind her back, because I knew it would make the others laugh. Her mum found out and told Fari and my father, John. Their disappointment in me as I sat in front of them in the formal lounge was almost as torturous as their instruction to hand-deliver a written letter of apology to her and her parents. I did it, shaking like a little pig-bird.

Mr Barrett, my year three teacher, doesn't make 'good' easy, either. He is a skinny man with a red face, who wears pressed shorts and long socks and shakes the boys by the shoulders when they make him angry. He never shakes girls. Instead, he makes us wait in the hallway for the principal to walk past. I usually crawl into the port racks and hide among the backpacks, forgotten swimming bags and mouldy bananas, in the hope that our principal, Mr Guilfoyle, won't see me. He always does.

I have at least seventeen vengeful thoughts about Mr Barrett every day, which is disappointing, because good people keep their thoughts and deeds pure. My primary sin is talking in his class. Also, messiness. Also, daydreaming. Oh, and everyone, especially my dad, thinks I'm too bossy – a flaw I plan to address through hope and prayer.

My dad is a very good man. Extraordinarily principled. He never backbites, or swears. He doesn't drink or smoke or gamble – not even a Lotto ticket. He's clean and tidy. He hangs the towels on the line without wasting pegs. He reads improving books and alphabetises our bookshelves – and we have a lot of books.

My eldest sister, Lisa, is Dad's favourite, even though he would never admit to having one. She's married to a good man, and even though she is beautiful and vain and spends far too much time in the bathroom, she's good too. My brother, Jamal, is always being scolded for kicking balls in the house and forgetting to mow the lawn, but Fari and my grandma, Dolly, love him like a god. A Rajah. He must be good.

But nobody – nobody – is as good as Rahnee.

Rahnee is Fari's favourite, even though she would never admit to having one. They move with the same spirit, laughing at the same jokes, seeing the world in the same colours. They even look the same. Black hair, olive skin, shiny eyes that crinkle at the corners. A book and its binding.

Rahnee is a school prefect. They gave her a gold badge to mark her goodness. Her side of our shared room is neat and tidy. She keeps a prayer book by her bed and under her pillow is a diary filled with messages, doodles, and folded paper frogs and love hearts from her friends. Whenever the phone rings it's for her. She wears the coolest clothes and pink frosty lipstick on her mouth, and Fari never tells her she can't. She's the only one Jamal treats with reverence. When I can't sleep she lets me hug her black teddy, Sooty, and she says I can have her Redline bike when she finishes school at the end of the year. She taught me how to use a pencil to fix a cassette when the tape spills out, and how to record songs off the radio so I can listen to them whenever I want.

Sometimes she pulls my long hair too hard when she's folding it into plaits.

'Go SOFTER!'

'Stay still. Don't you want to look like Pippi Longstocking?'

Pippilotta Delicatessa Windowshade Mackrelmint Ephraim's Daughter Longstocking is my hero. I spend most school afternoons perched on top of our broken tennis shed, pretending to be her, some toy or other strapped to my shoulder like Mr Nilsson, Pippi's monkey. I like to wear shirt dresses, knee socks, and my hair in plaits, just like her. I figure if being good doesn't work out, piracy is my only alternative.

Rahnee's boyfriend, Ashley, is a broad-shouldered giant with a golden, curly mullet. He never calls me 'Sita-the-girl' or 'snotface' like Jamal's friends do. He calls me 'cutie' and watches *Scooby-Doo* with me, sharing his chips. Whenever he calls Fari 'Mrs Walker' she smiles and says coyly, 'Ashley, don't you know my name?'

'Oh sorry, sorry, it's Queen Walker, isn't it?' he replies with a little bow, and Fari laughs and offers him biscuits or cake or whatever is in her hands, and he eats it in one bite. I see her smile at him when he's not looking.

When Ashley is in our room, Rahnee shuts the door, and shuts me out.

'I'll give you twenty cents if you go away.'

'Make it fifty.'

I take her money and lie on the floor of the hallway, ear to the carpet, spying under the door, trying to hear what's being said over U2's 'All I Want is You'. Sometimes I flick little balls of paper under, trying to hit their ankles. Sometimes Ashley flings open the door and chases me like a bear, or Rahnee opens the door and hisses, 'Go away or I'm never doing your hair again.' Sometimes their feet disappear and I wonder where they went.

I'm the last of the Walkers. The baby by almost a decade. Jamal likes to refer to me as 'the accident', but my dad always corrects him. He says I was 'a pleasant surprise'. We live on Bridge Street in a big country house with wooden walls, a tin sheet roof, and a long hallway down the middle, sprouting bedrooms. The ceilings are high and filled with light, and the windows big enough for two kids to climb in at the same time. There's an outhouse lined with spiders, peeling linoleum on the kitchen floor, and back steps that need painting. The house grumbles and tilts, but Bridge Street is simply the most wonderful place on earth. There's never a room without some-body in it, and God lives in the walls.

Our town, Toowoomba, is built in a crater-bowl and surrounded by mountain ranges. It's so high up that in the morning the fog cuts the roofs off houses, and at night the moon seems close enough to hold.

Mr Barrett taught me that before it was colonised, Toowoomba was a swamp. The settlers came and drove out the people of the swamp, then they drained and pummelled the fleshy ground into submission. They cleared and tilled fields and fenced paddocks. They built houses and churches and schools. The water flowing into the bowl from the sky and the mountains was channelled by man-made culverts and streams – a series of creeks and waterways that led it through the hills and into the west.

When summer turns to autumn, the wind blows over the mountains and fills the bowl, swirling and sweeping leaves into little tornados. It's the kind of wind that whips the cheeks of children red, and puts young men in a dangerous mood.

Toowoomba is a place where flowers grow through the cracks in the pavement. They say it's the swamp trying to push its way back to the surface. They say that, but what they mean is: eventually, all deeply buried things find their way up through the cracks.

The last time I saw my sister Rahnee she was riding the Redline down the side of our house, and I was running after her, asking for a turn.

That summer, the summer of 89, when Rahnee and Ashley died, the whole town wept. The creeks and streams ran high with it, flowing and gushing into the culverts and through the mountains and down into the valley where my sister and Ashley and three other kids were found, unconscious in a rolled car.

And the wind?

The wind brought my aunts to Bridge Street.

Aunty Irie cooked for days, weeping as she stirred and seasoned, red-faced and sweating at the stove. Chicken and lamb curries, brown lentil soup with generous handfuls of coriander and mint, yellow lentil spiced dahl, her special red macaroni cheese – creamy inside and golden on top. Food piled up in our kitchen like we were catering a Maharashtrian wedding.

Aunty Mona prayed. She prayed over everyone. She took us out into the garden and cuddled us close to her cotton island kaftan, and prayed and prayed and prayed. The constant sound of her murmuring and chanting became background noise, like the sound of test cricket over the summer.

Aunty Mehri walked up and down the length of our home like a headmistress. She cleaned and tidied efficiently and without rest. She welcomed guests. She told people when to leave and when to go to bed. She didn't sleep. She didn't smile. She made beds and hung out sheets and towels, and watched over us all like a wolf. She watched my dad especially well. Watched and waited.

My grandmother Dolly hovered over her four daughters, and followed me wherever I went.

I wore a pink dress to the funeral, my ankles blistering in white court shoes, my neck sweating under my loose hair. At the gravesite my father read the prayer for the dead, and Mehri held me on her lap, her scarlet sari silken under my dangling legs.

Leaning back and putting my lips to her ear, I whispered 'Aunty, my shoes hurt.'

'Take them off. Put your feet on the grass. It's okay,' she said. Her voice strong. Her chest tight.

I took off the shoes. The grass that was soon to cover my sister felt cool and fresh under my hot feet. Mehri turned me to face her.

'We have to be strong, Sita-koo. Like this,' she said in a low voice, balling her fist tightly and holding it next to her heart.

I put my fist up to my chest and squeezed it tight, looking into her dark eyes.

'Good,' she said. 'You're a good girl.'

A light went out that day, and I didn't cry at all.

1952. Panchgani.

Fari hitches up the woollen skirt of her navy-blue uniform and tucks it into her underpants, her fingers and mouth purple with mulberry juice. Up she goes, one branch at a time, climbing through the purpley-green haze to the top of the tree, snatching the choicest berries on the way up. The tree is high on a plateau, but here on the world's hilltop, everything is high. When she reaches the peak, sitting on the sturdiest brackened branch she can find, she parts the greenery, snaps a few small stalks off and picks away the berries before letting them drop to the ground. She gazes out at the valley, her brown eyes hazel in the glow.

Panchgani sits in the middle of five hills in the Sahyadri mountain ranges, in Maharashtra. A jewel in the emerald ring of India. The river Krishna flows like an open serpent through the foothills of the mountains. Fari watches it turn golden and mauve in the setting sun as she pops sweet balls of juice into her mouth, and wipes the purple dribble away with the back of her hand. It drips down into the cuff of her white uniform sleeve, and her bare feet swing in the way only a little girl's can. Her toes like brown buttons.

She should be back at school for prep and prayers, but she knows this evening, he will come. She knows it in her heart. She knows it like she knows how she will convince Shivani Khanum not to send her to Nargis Khanum for a beating and scolding tonight. It doesn't matter anyway, because seeing him will be worth ten beatings. Seeing him will be something to tell Neymat and Irie. Something extraordinary. She waits and watches, shifting slightly on her branch, but not disturbing the leaves.

Once, matron Shivani Khanum told her that she would not punish her for spoiling her best going-out dress if she pulled one hundred grey hairs from her head. Fari said yes, knowing the task would be impossible. Khanum didn't have many greys, and she was as vain as a Rajah's peacock. Slyly, Fari pulled out one grey hair, and showed it to Shivani. Then, she proceeded to pull out black hairs, and pass them backhanded to her sister Irie, all the while showing Khanum the same one grey hair, and making warm comments about her beauty, her youth, and her long black locks. Not only did she escape a beating, but Shivani washed her tea-stained going-out dress herself, and brought it back pressed.

The valley is painted in post-monsoon mixed greens. Indian green, hothouse green, forest and lime and jade. The air is mossy and fresh, and the insects buzz. Fari lets a beetle crawl onto the back of her hand.

'Hello little bug. Have you seen him? Where is he?' she whispers, stroking orange wings with her blackened finger.

A shimmer and the beetle flies away. Fari's eyes follow it to the base of the tree. She sees a black shadow pass underneath, and her body turns to ice.

It is him.

The panther strides out from under the tree, making its way down the hillside. Slowly. Perfectly. A ballet of black. Fari holds her breath and sits like a stone, watching his muscular shoulders roll his velvety body as he strides through the long grass and strawberry vines, stalking like a pool of hot tar towards a little copse of trees. Here, he pauses, puts his nose to the ground and stills, taking in a scent. Suddenly, his head is turned back and lifted upwards, pointing directly at the mulberry tree. Fari can swear he is looking right at her with his yellow cat eyes. For a second, they are joined like lovers in the gloaming. She closes her eyes quickly, not to allow him inside her, not to let him stalk back and scale the tree and eat her whole, bones and all. The crunch of her little body would be like a pappadum in his slick jaws.

Trembling, eyes vice-closed, she grips the branch of the tree and whispers her magic prayer, over and over:

'Oh God, guide me, protect me, make of me a shining lamp and a brilliant star

'Oh God, guide me, protect me, make of me a shining lamp and a brilliant star

'Oh God, guide me, protect me, make of me a shining lamp and a brilliant star.'

When she opens her eyes, the valley is empty. She is alone.

Twelve months ago.

At 5pm my phone pings.

Fingerprint recognition isn't working. I swipe up and tap in my passcode. I click into the little yellow hive icon. It's him.

Been a little held up, can we say 515? Sorry x

I send the thumbs-up emoji, hoping this isn't a man who is always late to everything.

The pub is quiet, and I've chosen a high table close to the bar under some warm, brass lamps. I feel self-conscious, like I should've tied my hair back, even though my outfit is understated. Jeans, tan boots and a grey cable-knit. My earrings are silver horses, dangling. My hair is long and shiny and I've spritzed it with perfume so that it smells like yellow freesia and rose. It's falling across my face. I look for a hair tie in my clutch.

Ping.

Thank you, was just co-ordinating a FaceTime with my little dude.

This is better. Another thumbs-up emoji, because I'm trying to be aloof and cool. The thumbs-up says: I'm busy and caught up in something other than you. I'm in demand. I've got things going on. I'm above your lateness.

I'm not. I'm kicking myself for getting here first. My insides are moths bumping into a fluorescent tube, and I can't find a hair tie.

A drink.

Brisbane Brewing is a relaxed micro-brewery in the city's bohemian West End. Steel vats line the walls. They're all about beer, but I order a dry prosecco. The Foo Fighters are playing just loud enough for me to have to raise my voice slightly to order. Should I be bold and buy him a beer so that it's on the table when he arrives? What kind of message does that send? That I'm thoughtful and cool? Or over-eager? What if he doesn't want beer? What if he's a vegetarian? What do I even mean by that? No beer. The barman looks at me as if he knows I'm here to meet someone, and I feel myself go red in the face. I take a sip of bubbles as I walk back to my stool. Tangy and crisp, like a Granny Smith.

I remember the first drink I ever had. I was twenty-eight, and had just weaned my second baby off my breast. Since Borhan's grand exodus from faith and followership, he had been having some sort of belated and extended O-week – reading Nietzsche, watching Richard Feynman talks about particle physics, and drinking Glenfiddich scotch whisky. For us, alcohol was strictly forbidden. It was against our religion. It weakened the mind and the spirit, and tarnished the purity of the drinker. Good, faithful, transcendent people did not drink. All throughout high school and university I never touched a drop – not even in a risotto or a plum pudding. But, with two small children and a husband experiencing a hedonistic renaissance, something came over me. I decided that God and I needed a little space. So at the end of a blustery afternoon wrangling small children, I stood at my kitchen bench, spilling over with sippy cups, plastic spoons and mashed apple, and I poured myself my maiden glass of red wine. The weight of goodness slipped away as I tentatively put the cup to my lips, like some sort of reverse communion.

It was revolting. I spat it out into the sink.

But it didn't matter. I felt exhilarated. Like I'd made a choice for myself. Like I'd made my very own mistake.

Ping.

I'll be there anon.

The actor speaks in prose.

I feel an excited tingle running down from my throat to my stomach, fizzing together with the bubbles of my prosecco. I imagine him quoting *Much Ado About Nothing* to me while he pours red wine into bolognaise, in the nook kitchen of our bohemian cottage in West End. I imagine his book collection – vast. His taste in music – eclectic. The Dandy Warhols and Johnny Cash, perhaps? Maybe some nineties grunge? I imagine he smokes occasionally, even though his profile said, 'smokes: never'. I imagine he likes to shower in the morning. I imagine he's into blondes, or businesswomen, or yoga instructors – not nerdy brunettes with three kids and neo-existentialist ex-husbands.

I adjust my stool so I can see the entrance to the pub, and text my best friend, Andy.

He's late.

Ping.

Ugh. Actors. It had better be because he was hit by a van.

He was on the phone to his kid.

Ping.

He has kids? How many? How old?

No idea. Shit he's here.

I slide my phone under my clutch, take one more sip of the Granny Smith, and stand up to kiss Anthony's gruff cheek for the very first time.

His greeting is warm and sincere, with a hint of mannered reserve. He smells good. Fresh. Blokey. He looks like he could be Russell Crowe's younger brother, but with less hair. We exchange pleasantries. I'm feeling awkward and haven't eased into the interaction with what anyone would call charm.

He puts his satchel down on the stool opposite me and goes to make for the bar, turning back sheepishly. 'I took a punt with the whole "be there anon" thing . . . coupla arvo wines. How'd that land?'

I grin. 'It was a first for me.'

2016. Brisbane.

I crawl under the white doona of my marital bed, in jeans, a t-shirt and sneakers, and pull it up over my head. I don't think I can do this. I managed to get the kids to school this morning, and to call in sick to work, but I'm not sick. I've just lost my will to live.

I can smell a sweaty tang on the floral sheets, and I wonder when I last washed them. Under the doona it's warm, and I breathe in my own air as the tears begin to fall down my cheeks, their saltiness mingling with the moisturiser on my face. And then I sob. Heaving sobs. Sobs so dramatic my chest begins to hurt.

Last night I had the dream again. It's always the same. I'm standing in the kitchen, or the lounge, and I'm chewing bubble-gum. A big glob of pink, rubbery gum. I decide to spit it out but it's sticking to my teeth, so I pull at it. I pull and pull and the gum keeps coming and coming. It's filling up my mouth, it's in my throat, I'm having trouble breathing but I can't call for help because my mouth is plugged up with gum. Just when I think I've pulled the last bit out, there's more rising up from my oesophagus – a never-ending pink goo glob.

I have this dream every few months, but last night it was particularly distressing. I woke up and gasped for air.

I reach for my phone, still sobbing, scroll down my recent calls and click on 'Ma'.

Two rings and she picks up. Two hours and she and my dad have driven down the mountain, across the valley and into Brisbane city. They are at my house. They let themselves in. Dad knocks politely on my open bedroom door and says jovially, 'Is my precious treasure under there somewhere?'

'I'm sorry you had to drive all the way here, Dad,' I gurgle from under the covers, before surfacing looking so wretched that my six-foot-four father crawls into the bed next to me, his long, broad back leaning up against the headboard, and scoops me up into his arms.

'There, there, dear. We're here, now. It's no trouble. What are parents for? We'll sort you out, darling.'

My mother is pacing up and down. 'Fari! Stop flapping about and make her a cup of tea, will you?'

Mum leans over Dad and kisses my cheek, feels my forehead with her palm and her wrist. She smells of Ponds day cream and turmeric. I feel a calmness hit my belly and start to spread out. A tear falls down my cheek but she wipes it away. 'Don't worry baby, Daddy will fix all of it. Just tell him what you need.' She turns on him, 'John-John, you fix it okay? Okay.' Like it's done. 'Sita, where are the kids? Are they all right?'

'They're at school, Ma.'

'Darling, tea. Off you go. I'll have one too, while you're at it,' Dad says with his usual efficacity. He pulls a neatly folded cotton handkerchief from his top pocket and offers it to me. I take it, and pat my face dry.

While Fari is brewing the tea and washing the pots and pans in my messed up kitchen, I tell my dad that I have so much to do, and I don't really know how to do it. I've told Borhan I'm moving out, but I need to find a house to rent. I need to file for divorce. I need to change my surname. I need to sort out the health insurance, and the Centrelink, and the Medicare. I need to buy a car. He pats my shoulder with his gigantic hand and gives the occasional hum of acknowledgement. I lean into his chest.

A noisy miner outside my window is peeping and chir-ruping to a rhythm. The cat wanders in and jumps up on my bed. Mum comes back with two cups of tea, hot, with a dash of milk. Lately she's been warning me about the dangers of sugar. Last time she was here she refused to put any more than half a teaspoon into my cup. Dad has been cut off completely.

I take a sip and the tea is sweet.

'Thanks, Ma.'

She sits on my other side, and there we are. Three in a row, with a saucy cat at our feet. Mum takes my free hand and puts it between hers.

'I'm going to say a prayer, baby. You'll see how magic it is, it will fix everything.'

I haven't prayed in years, but I nod. Dad slurps his tea and says, 'Your mother will pray, and then I'll call Medicare.'

1957. Sydney.

John sharpened his pencil and breathed out a sigh. Latin. What was the point? Enduring French was bad enough, but Latin? There was simply no rational reason he should have to translate Julius Caesar's account of the Gallic wars from Latin to English. It had been done. His Trinity Grammar Latin master, Mr Horrocks, was tall and thin, sharp and pointed. A pencil of a man. He liked to sweep about in his academic gown, conjugating verbs with relish. John fingered his collar and imagined his stick-straight teacher sinking into quicksand. He smiled.

John's mind was not on Latin. It was on Mohammad. The only theological stumbling block he encountered with the Bahá'í teachings was the question of Mohammad.

John's mother, Margaret Jeanette Walker, loved him. She taught him to cook, to sew, to clean and polish floors, to hang out the washing neatly without wasting pegs. She encouraged his studies and always made sure he left the house with a freshly pressed handkerchief in his pocket. She was particular, neat and meticulous, with a will that could no more be broken or bent than a steel girder on the Harbour Bridge. Margaret enjoyed spotless floors, a nicely pressed linen frock, and several dry sherries after dinner. She did not enjoy divorcing her husband because he decided to leave the bank, join some hippy, communist religion and spend his time with people whose names she couldn't pronounce. Nor did she enjoy that 'Bahá'í shindig' infecting her tall, handsome, well-educated son.

It was best, Margaret thought, that John be confirmed in the Anglican Church. As soon as possible.

John was not so sure.

He had secretly read his father's books on the Bahá'í faith, hiding them under his mattress, or at the back of the linen cupboard. He was taken with it. He could not understand his mother's prejudice, or how this religion of love and unity could be the source of a feud that had ended his parents' marriage. He thought it a sensible religion in every way. There was just the pesky issue of Mohammad.

The faith taught that Mohammad was a Manifestation of God, just like Jesus Christ, or Moses, Buddha and Krishna. But the schoolboy image John had of Islam was of Mohammad spreading his word by the sword, or lounging in an orgiastic chamber, surrounded by forty wives. Saladin, violently slicing his way through Africa. Conquered peoples given the choice of conversion or death. He had to find out more.

To buy himself some time and appease his mother, John told her that he would attend all the divinity classes required prior to confirmation, and then make up his mind.

He had spent the last week at the school library, nose-deep in the *Encyclopaedia Britannica* and *Gibbon's History of the Decline and Fall of the Roman Empire* – the only two places he could find anything written down about Islam. But it was not enough to be really sure about Mohammad. John realised that he needed to read the Koran. The problem was, he couldn't get one. Trinity Grammar didn't have one. The library didn't have one. Perhaps his father had one, but he was selling life insurance in Mudgee, living in a boarding house, and there were only two trains out there a week. It was a real pickle, made worse by his mother pressuring him to commit himself to the Anglican Church, forever.

In divinity class, John had asked his teacher, the Reverend Michaels, about Islam. Michaels was young and not too bright. He had an air of self-importance in his dog collar. He was not universally liked.

'The first thing you need to know about Islam is that Muslims are pagans!' said Reverend Michaels.

'What is a pagan, sir?' asked John.

'A pagan is someone who doesn't believe in God.'

'Sir, that's an atheist.'

The class was still. Now he had their attention.

'Well . . . they're heathens then!' said Michaels, eyeballing John as though he were a fly in his soup.

'Sir, what is a heathen?' asked John, politely.

'Heathens are people who don't believe in Jesus Christ.'

Well, this did not align with the evidence presented in John's research.

'Sir, I've been doing a bit of reading about Islam, and I understand that Muslims do believe that Jesus was a prophet of God. They believe that he was the spirit of God, born of the Virgin Mary and that his word was the word of God.'

The tips of Michaels' ears coloured plum.

'Well, they don't believe he *is* God, do they?' he spat.

John was unperturbed. Actually, he was rather enjoying himself. The class hummed in anticipation of his next move.

'I've got an uncle who is a minister in the Anglican church,' John said, 'who thinks that the trinity is meant to be taken metaphorically and not literally.'

This was all too much for Michaels. He marched over to John's desk, rapped on it with his pink knuckles, and said: 'Walker. I'll discuss this with you later.'

When the class was finished and the boys had begun filing out, the Reverend called John over to his desk.

'Walker. Don't you ever do that again.'

'Do what, sir?'

'If you ever, ever, do that again, you'll be cut from the athletics team. Do you understand?'

John did. He understood that prejudice was irrational. Michaels didn't know anything about Islam and yet he had begun his discussion about it with a prejudicial statement. His mother was the same. She knew nothing about the Bahá'í faith, and yet she despised it because of what other people would think. The only thing divinity class had confirmed in John was that ignorance and prejudice were two heads of the same beast. And that beast was pride.

John went home to his mother that afternoon and said, 'Mum, I know what you want, but I'm not ready to be confirmed, or to make any statement of faith just yet.'

Margaret pursed her lips, pushed a length of tweed cloth through her sewing machine, and didn't say a word.

1963. Pune.

Fari sits cross-legged on the divan, worrying her swollen bottom lip with her top teeth. She pulls the damp cotton cloth from her shoulder, waves it around in the hot, spiced air of the Indian summer before rolling it roughly and putting it back on her neck. Next to her, Irie sleeps on her stomach, breathing heavily, her head on her hands, feet pigeon-toed together, wrinkled soles facing the paint-peeled cement ceiling of their bedroom. Her rose nightie is damp to her back. The sprawling mecca of Pune can be unbearably hot in July, but the monsoon will bring relief.

On the other divan, her eldest cousin sleeps soundly, and three others lie top to toe on the floor mattress, the fingers of moonlight reaching through the window lattice to paint checks on their lanky, brown limbs. Her older sisters, Mehri and Mona, have married and gone. There is more room on the floor now.

The moon waxed full last night, and as it sinks, Fari can hear the jangle of the chai vendor's cart and the early cry of a red-whiskered bulbul. She is too excited to sleep. Her mother, Dolly, has been in Bombay for two months. Today she will arrive home, and with her, Neymat.

Fari's cousin Neymat reminds her of Dilip Kumar, the Hindi film actor. Bollywood's answer to Cary Grant. Neymat is not as handsome, and he's skinny as a Calcutta monkey of course, but he teases just like a film star and smiles just as broadly. He's kind, naughty, and always smells like soap and biscuits, which he shares only with her.

Irie always says that Neymat and Fari are 'two of a kind. Too good, too bad and too much.' When he comes home they are going to see a film called *Hum Dono* – 'Both of Us' – with Dilip Kumar and Sadhana Shivdasani. All of her friends have seen it, but Fari wants to wait for Neymat.

Fari is obsessed with Sadhana, and has taken great pains to look exactly like her, on no budget. But she doesn't need to imitate. Almond eyes, long black plait reaching down to the crest of her backside, a figure that could part waves. Fari is a beauty. She takes classical Indian dance lessons, moving like a lotus flower in bangles, and even though she was the naughtiest girl at her school in Panchgani, always cutting class, always dishevelled from climbing trees and walls, everybody smiles when they say her name. With the right kind of connections, she could have been a film star, but now that she's twenty, she's decided an air hostess is the profession for her. Glamorous. Adventurous. Her sister Irie is being courted by a pilot from New Delhi. They've been exchanging letters for months. Maybe it isn't such an outrageous idea, if she can marry well.

When they were little – all twelve of them, living on the bottom floor of the two-bedroom bungalow with Dolly, her widowed sister, Firooza, and Koloo – their tireless ayah – Neymat and Fari were inseparable. None of the children had a father. Both men were lost to disease. The four boys, Fari's spectacular big brother, Khodi, and her three cousins, constantly sweaty from street cricket, soccer, and squeezing the ears of stray dogs, all slept in one room with her formidable aunt, Firooza. Firooza and the boys were father enough for the eight girls bunked in the other. Dolly and Koloo slept on the open verandah, fanning themselves with woven bamboo and laughing together. In the daytime they would shell peas, soak lentils and rice, hang rows of handwashed clothes over lines of string between the bungalow trees. When you have twelve children to feed, there isn't much else you can do.

Sometimes, on a night like this one when the moon was high enough and Firooza lay long and stiff, puffing snores, Fari and Neymat would sneak out and sleep under the stars in the park across the street. They would lie under the banyan trees, hold hands, talk about films and laugh like otters. The banyan trees drew their laughter into cascading roots, sending it down into the earth and up into the sky over the subcontinent.

They were too old for that now. People would talk.

Dawn broke with a jangle of carts and trolleys, bike tyres, brown voices greeting and hawking, and the squeak of double-decker buses on nearby Railway Road. Fari turned the letter over in her hands, reading it again in the new light:

Fari-jaan,

I am coming home. The Faith is spreading here, and people are understanding what it means to be one with each other and God, but I miss Pune. I miss you. When will we see *Hum Dono* together? It is still playing, I hope? Don't let them take it down. Go fight them like a tigress. I will help you hide your lipstick from Aunty. Let's pick oranges and suck the peels before we throw them into Sanjay fatso-walla's rickshaw.

See you soon, bulbul.
Neymat

Dolly arrived home at noon that day to a gaggle of family all hugging and pulling. Fari held back.

'Maman, Neymat kahaan hai?'

'He wasn't at the station,' she said, taking her into her arms. 'Perhaps he will arrive on the next bus, hah? He won't be long, beta. Monsoon is coming.'

There are places in the world where people talk to God so much they think they know His will. They take God's name and fashion it into a sword, or a bomb, or a gun, or a knife. Then they use it against anyone who tries to say they heard God differently.

Khodi found Neymat's broken body splayed out under a bodhi tree in a gully. Glass in his skin. The blood dry. The tampered car wrapped around a tree. He had been teaching the faith to the wrong kinds of people; people who think God sits in their ear, alone. Wailing and hurling, Khodi dragged his cold cousin out before the sky broke and the Mithi River had the chance to take him out to sea.

Fari took death's hand for the first time, and didn't let it go for twenty-seven years.

Twelve months ago.

Anthony is picking at the remains of my burger and chips, and we're laughing. He has just told me the best romcom is *Notting Hill*, that he is such a Richard Curtis tragic he can quote whole scenes verbatim, along with entire seasons of *Blackadder*. I ask him to prove it, but he says, 'Maybe next time,' with a sincere smile.

He seems to be very good at this – dating, being himself. He makes me laugh. He laughs at me. He asks questions, hand-to-brow, and holds my gaze steadily while I answer. He says 'fuck' a lot and it sounds like poetry. He is just as comfortable discussing seventies American cinema as he is taking the piss out of his country high school musical, a fruity romp set in the Arabian Desert: *Sheik, Rattle and Roll*.

He has a kind face, and what's left of his hair is buzzed short. He's got a salt-and-pepper trimmed beard that makes him look older than what he is, and broad shoulders. He's solid, and a bit rugger, but the gruffness is belied by notes of flamboyance. He crosses his legs elegantly, he speaks with his hands, he uses words like 'dogmatic' and 'saccharine' and 'elemental'.

Talk turns to his boy, who lives up north with his mum. He gives little away but the situation seems complicated. Every time he mentions his son his eyes flicker downward for a second and the tenor of his voice shifts, something in him moves. I'm turned on by it, this pain, something under the surface coming through the cracks, the thought that if he is a bit broken then he will be able to face my brokenness. I wish I had let him talk more, instead of nervously talking about myself for most of the night, but his gaze was hard to resist.

The pub is winding down. The barman is polishing glasses and glances our way.

We finish our drinks. The actor smiles, his blue-grey steady on me.

'Can I walk you to your car?'

'Sure, thanks. I just need to use the ladies'.'

In the tin and steel trendy bathroom I text Andy and tell her that I'm leaving the pub, but she can stand down. I'm quite sure he's not going to murder me. He's an artist. If he is going to kill me it will be slowly, with thirty years of fighting, blazing and pedantry, not tonight with a knife. She's pleased. She wants details but she'll have to wait. I read a text from Ma from two hours ago: *you home? Kids asleep?* I look in the mirror and fix one eyebrow that's gone a bit skew-whiff. I pull the cable-knit v-neck down as low as it will go, and adjust my bra so that the top curves of my breasts are showing just a bit.

What if he kisses me? Do people kiss at the end of first dates, nowadays? They do in *Notting Hill*. I haven't kissed many men in my life, but enough to know that a kiss can change the way you see someone, show you the shape of things. I pop a stick of minty gum in my mouth and chew fast, yanking up my jeans to check my butt out in the mirror. You want him to kiss you, I think, but push it away. I swirl the gum around while I wash and dry my hands, and then spit it into the paper towel bin.

We walk out into the street. It's been raining. The warmth of the day is still hanging about but there's a crisp breeze blowing pockets of warm and cool past us. The night has moved quickly. Time has slipped away and now Anthony is strolling beside me. I wonder if he will try to hold my hand, but he doesn't. He walks steadily, chats easily.

We pass the Bearded Lady, a guitar noodling softly, glasses clinking, a couple smoking outside. She's wearing a long velvet dress. We pass the Greek real estate agent where I rented The Shack, but I don't tell him about it. At the car, I offer to give him a lift back to the guest house where he's staying, but he says it's not far to walk.

'Hey,' he says softly.

'Yeah?'

Anthony kisses me with one hand on my waist and the other on my face.

'Hi,' I manage.

He kisses me again and gently holds the hair on the back of my head, while his other hand pulls me in. A glimpse of the blue-grey and he kisses me a third time. He's quiet. Both hands hold my face like a jewel. I feel all spun-out, moonstruck. I lean into him and put my hand on his chest, our mouths together, our stomachs touching. Strains of Bollywood music from the Indian restaurant on the corner, tyres rushing on the wet road, the smell of fried food and beer and dirty petrichor, and him.

We open our eyes. West End is still there.

'That was delightful . . .' I say.

He smiles like a boy as his hands slip from my waist and into his jacket pockets.

That was delightful (!)

I start up the Falcon and run the wipers over the wet windscreen. Matchbox Twenty is playing on the radio. The Lebanese kebab place is closing its roller doors. Two skinny men are doing a drug handshake outside the 7-Eleven. It's not until I reach the top of Highgate Hill that I realise I'm crying.

1990. Toowoomba.

It's November and the jacarandas are turning my town purple. Mrs Wickham, our bespectacled year four teacher, a big shock of red hair cascading over her shoulder pads, is reading the class a story. I'm sitting on the parquetry floor next to my best friend, Kitty Cordner. Kitty has two long blonde plaits tied with pink and red bobble hair ties that I love but my mother won't buy me. The louvres are open, and the hot, after-lunch air is being pushed lazily around by a tin ceiling fan. I didn't get time to go to the toilet at big lunch, because Kitty and I were playing marbles – for keeps. We have a joint collection in an old denim pencil case. One night she takes it home, the next I do. We guard it like mother magpies. Galaxies, steelies, bigs, peewees, plenty of cats' eyes. We have so many marbles the zip is threatening to bust.

At big lunch, Jasper Stegalls challenged us to a keepsies game, and even though we always swore we would only play funsies with Jasper (because Kitty loves him) we changed our minds when he said he would bet his milko blood splash. Jasper has long golden-beach hair, an undercut and pale blue eyes with dark lashes. He is the first boy who ever made me look twice.

We didn't win. We lost a big galaxy, and Kitty cried in front of everyone. Jasper laughed with his friends. Scott Stevens kicked an orange at us and said, 'As if youse girls could beat us, you're such retards.'

I hugged Kitty and shouted at him, 'I know you are but what am I?' He flipped me the bird. His middle fingernail was chewed down to the quick.

Mrs Wickham licks her thumb to turn the page. We are lost in the alphabet magic of *Animalia* by Graeme Base.

I wipe the sweat beads off my upper lip, and brush my hair out of my face with my palm. I haven't eaten. My grandmother Dolly packed me a green bean sandwich in cling-wrap for lunch. All we have had this week is beans because she got a sack of them on special from her Vietnamese friend at the Sunday markets. Bean curry, bean stew, steamed beans, bean and lentil dahl, beans in tomato rice. Yesterday she started with the bean sandwiches. Bread, a smear of butter, and a handful of raw beans. There was no way I was eating that in front of Kitty, who always had a neatly packed ham and butter sandwich and a Popper. Fari and Dolly didn't believe in Poppers. Juice came out of fruit, not little cardboard boxes.

Every day one of us gets to have *Animalia* to ourselves after reading time, to try and find the secrets hidden in the alliterated pictures. Tigers on their way to Timbuktu. Crayfish cavorting with cats. It is the blue butterfly that takes me. I love caterpillars and bugs and little jumping, flying things – bees, grasshoppers, moths. The blue butterfly's sky-wings shimmer by a babbling brook. There are pictures hidden in the wings but I can't make them out at a distance; they are too delicate, too faint. I've been waiting weeks to hold the book up to my nose and sink into it. Today it is my turn. Mrs Wickham turns to the last page and I clench my jaw in anticipation. My body gives a slight shiver as a slow trickle of water begins running down my inner thigh. The trickle becomes a warm gush. Before I can think, hot piss starts to pool on the parquetry under my folded legs. I freeze like a possum in torchlight and tuck my legs in tight. I clench my bottom and push a cupped hand into my crotch, but I can't stop the flow. It keeps coming and coming. The horror is only matched by the relief.

I don't move. I stare at Mrs Wickham as she finishes the book, begging her with my eyes. Tell the class to go back to their seats. Tell them before they see. Moving my arms slowly, I spread my dress out as far as it can go, around my back and over my folded legs, trying to create a barrier to seal in the puddle. I hold my breath hoping others won't smell the vinegary tang. My socks are sopping. My ankles itch.

'Look at all those zigzagging zebras!' she enthuses. 'Isn't that clever? Now whose turn is it to take the book today?'

Mrs Wickham was kind. She saw my wide eyes, red, blinking away tears, saw the soggy mess beneath me. She dropped down a towel, shielding me with her wide skirt as I stood up, dripping. I stared at her ruched-vinyl belt buckle as she asked Kitty to take me down to the hall locker and help me 'freshen up', slipping a plastic bag from the Chinese takeaway into my hand.

Her skirt wasn't enough to protect me. They all knew.

After school, Kitty thumbed her plaits and told me she didn't want to share marbles anymore, because it was 'getting too hard to remember who had won them'. It was my turn to take them home that night. I said I'd split them up and give her half on Monday, and I walked home alone.

Bridge Street ran through what is now the gentrified, eastern side of town, but we lived there before it was posh. The front of the house was lined with bottlebrush trees, crowded together, long willowy branches holding the red flowers like fuzzy hands. A grass and dirt driveway passed the house to meet a two-car garage and half an acre of land. My treed kingdom.

The house smelled of pan ghee and cumin seeds. I dumped my schoolbag on the kitchen floor and wrapped my arms around my grandmother Dolly, handing her the Chinese takeaway parcel of shame. She had a cursory look, squeezed my face, and underarmed the whole bag into the washing basket.

'Come, Baba, eat this,' she said, scooping out a sizzling batch of bean, onion and potato pakoras and tossing them onto a plate of paper towels.

My brother, Jamal, nineteen and smelling of grass stains and sweat, was peeling his drenched socks and shin pads off to throw in the wash. He fished the bag out and read the attached note: 'Sita had a little accident at school today.'

'Little accident?' he laughed cruelly. 'And check it out!' he said, pointing earnestly to my shirt with his tanned finger, 'you've spilled some sauce.' I looked down and he flicked my nose up, squeezed it hard and pulled me into a spoony head-lock.

'Now. Say, "Men are the best".'

'Men are the best,' I said flatly. Limp in his arms.

He loosened his grip and eyed me, frowning. 'Don't worry about it, Small. Next week they'll have someone new to pick on.' Then he spun me around and rubbed his sweaty head all over my cheek.

After dinner I curled up next to my mother on the couch. *Sale of the Century* was on and Dad was winning over the stable table Grandma placed on his long thighs. Fari, in a soft button-down house dress, sat silent on the bamboo lounge. She thumbed her wooden prayer beads and stared through the telly, like she had done for twelve months.

My mother had always been the brightest light in the house. Since Rahnee's accident, she was a ghost.

I put my head on her shoulder and my knees on her lap, trying to see what she saw. I tried to find my mother past Tony Barber, past the tongue and groove wall, past the kingdom, with its clover grass and tennis-shed cubby; the overgrown court, the orange tree, the enormous camphor laurel that held every single one of my secrets and dreams. A tear fell down my face and onto her arm. She stirred and turned to me. Mine again for a moment.

I whispered to her what had happened. How the kids had laughed when the bell went, how Scott Stevens had called me a baby, how Kitty had walked in silence with me to the hall locker: 'She didn't say any words, Ma.' How my wee had turned the towel yellow, how I wished I could have apple and strawberry Poppers at school, how I had to split up the marbles but I didn't know which ones to keep and which ones to give to Kitty. How I never wanted to go back again.

'Shh, shh, shh,' Dad shushed me, his hand flapping. 'These chaps are tied after the fast money.'

Dolly shuffled over and put a small bowl of crumbled pistachio halwa in Mum's hand, slipping a piece of it into my mouth. Mum lowered her voice and spoke softly to me while Tony asked the 'Who am I?' tie-breaker. The halwa melted on my tongue.

'Sita mine, in life we are all standing in a circle, holding hands. Whatever you give away will come right back to you,' she said, putting her arm around me and squeezing me tight. 'When you go back to school, just forget about yourself completely.'

'How?'

'Easy. By doing something for someone else.'

'But I don't want to go back,' I said, tearing up. Puddling into her.

'George Bush!' Dad's bowl of ice-cream leapt from his lap.

'You will go back, and there will be no problems for you, don't worry baby. I'm going to pray for that little friend of yours, so she can become stronger.'

For a minute my mother was herself again. She stood up, took the tea towel from Dad's stable table and dabbed at the spots of ice-cream on his shirt. Dad covered her hand with his and gave it a squeeze without looking up from the television.

My mother and father were like the sea and the sky. Different worlds, unable to be parted at the horizon.

That night, Fari tucked me into bed again. She sat with me and scratched my back gently, and for the first time in months, I had my Ma back.

On Monday, I gave Kitty Cordner all the marbles, and walked away from her without saying a word.

Twelve months ago.

'Andy, he kissed me and then I cried in the car. All the way home.'

My best friend, Andy, and I are brunching together, in different cities. I'm on my leafy back deck in Brissy, she's in her glass greenhouse in Canberra, perched among the pots, finger-less gloves wrapped around a mug. Her brown face lights up my phone, a mass of curls atop.

'Seets, just tell me what happened. From the beginning. I'm sure it's all normal,' Andy says in her best psychology voice, taking a bite of toast.

It's helpful to have a friend who is a trauma counsellor. She's counselled children whose parents were hanging from beams in the next room; refugees who have watched their families murdered; inmates who've caused brutal road accidents or committed homicide, but she's still always available to foren-sically analyse my middle-class problems.

'I've told you everything. We had an amazing night, then he walked me to my car, then he kissed me, I said "that was delightful" like a moron, and then had some sort of Diane Keaton–esque breakdown.'

'Did he see you crying in the car?'

'No, no! He walked away. I'd driven off.'

'Was it a kiss, kiss? Like a pash kiss?' she asks with a saucy grin.

We are thirty-nine.

'Yes, it was a pash kiss!' Now I'm grinning. 'He kisses like Joseph Fiennes in *Shakespeare in Love*. Soft, but strong, you know? He held my face, Ands. It was goooood.'

'Oh my god, that's so good,' she says reverently.

'It's very good.' I nod.

We sip our tea. Andy diagnoses: 'I think the crying was just a decompression. It's no big deal. You've had a stressful few

THE GOD OF NO GOOD

months, years, a mad decade, really. A tender moment like that can trigger things. It's really helpful to find that release. How do you feel today? Still tearful?'

'No, I'm fine today, but maybe the crying meant that I've made a mistake? That I shouldn't be doing this.'

'Doing what? Enjoying a night out with an interesting man who makes you laugh and kisses like a movie star? I think this all sounds perfect for you. The only thing you're guilty of is overthinking. You were overthinking when he kissed you, weren't you?'

'No, I wasn't.' (Definitely was.)

'Go out with him again and just have a good time. Please. I beg you. Have fun. Enjoy the moment. See what happens.'

Ping.

'Oh my god he just messaged me on Bumble.'

'What? Read it. Read it out.'

I read his message. I snort a giggle.

'What does it say?!'

'It says: "My number: 0491577644. That was delightful x".'

Andy's perfect white smile lights up my screen. 'You have my full permission to go kiss this man again.'

1966. The Indian Ocean. South of Ceylon.

It is midnight and still. Fari makes her way upwards, climbing the narrow steps to the deck of the SS *Oronsay*, soundless and barefoot, her hair loosely plaited and hanging low. She moves like liquid through lifeboats and davits, wandering aft to find a secluded spot where she can grasp the railing of the stern and peer out to sea, back towards Ceylon. The Indian Ocean is calm in the blackness. No crested waves or rolling swell. Hardly even a sea wind. The only sound is the reassuring throb of the *Oronsay* vibrating under her bare feet, and the watery pulse of froth left behind as the passenger liner cuts neatly through the sea.

They have been journeying for seven days now. The *Oronsay* came from London, and is making its way to Australia via the Orient. Khodi is there. He left his mother, his sisters, and his gaggle of cousins, and started a new life by marrying an Australian girl he met in Panchgani – Joan.

After Neymat was killed, Khodi grieved and drifted. He was a handsome lad, tall and broad, and a jokester of the brightest and best order, but his spirit was gentle and kind; paternal and protective. He was Dolly's only son, her north star, her Rajah. When he suffered the loss of his best friend, and the closest thing he had to a brother in that world of angels and demons, fighting was never an option. Instead, he chose flight. The same year they buried Neymat, Khodi met Joan and boarded a plane to Australia with her. Dolly's blood had turned to cold soup with missing him. One beautiful boy taken to God, another to the end of the earth.

Fari wondered what Joan was like. Could Khodi ever be married to anyone good enough for him? Could any woman love him as much as his sisters did? Fifteen days at sea and they would find out.

From the palm-lined Colombo Harbour, Dolly, Mona and Fari, along with Mona's five small children, waved goodbye to Mehri at the dock, and were ferried out to board the *Oronsay*. The hulking figure was anchored offshore, its terraced decks and portholes catching the peach light of the setting Ceylonese sun. She was twenty-five, but Fari had never seen such a thing. The swaying 'tourist class' passenger ferry that had taken them out to the ship was primitive, and the women's sandals were soaked through; the hem of Fari's muslin sari wet and sticking to her ankles, little blue flowers darkened by the water.

She grasped Mona's son Nabil's small hand as he chirruped, 'Dekho, Aunty! Aunty, look!'

Curio vendors selling tourist fodder from bumboats had rowed out to meet the liner, hawking and transferring their wares onto the ship via ropes. Little carved figurines, mostly. Tigers, elephants in rows, ornamental bowls engraved with palm trees and monkeys. Fari had a small suitcase and no money for trinkets.

'Baba jaan, those aren't for us. Look! Look at the ropes going up to the Rajah's at the top! Fatso-walla's with their toy tigers,' she said, puffing out her cheeks and crossing her eyes at him.

Nabil laughed good-naturedly, for never was there a sweeter soul. 'Let's go up too, Aunty!'

Soosun chimed in, her pigtails bouncing. 'Yes, let's go! Chalo, chalo!'

'Achha, meree jaan,' Fari said, pulling Nabil up onto her hip, his little sandal dripping saltwater down her sari.

Okay, my darlings.

Now, they were asleep. Curled up like mice in a tiny cabin with their mother, Mona, and Dolly, bound for a new world. Fari wondered if they would stay there. Grow up Australian. Speak in broad, salted English, like Joan did. Dolly had no plans to return to India, but Fari thought she might not be able to live in a country filled with crocodiles and surrounded by crashing waves. In his letters, Khodi said that Australia was 'big and clean', and that's exactly what the Australian children on the ship were. Big and clean and golden, like warriors before a battle. They looked as though if you threw them overboard they could swim home laughing on the backs of whales. Next to them, Mona's children were five tiny starfish with wide eyes.

Earlier this evening, after dinner, an Englishman had approached Fari on the balcony of the dining room, 'Would you like to go up to the sun deck and see the stars with me, my dear?'

'No, thank you, I can't. I'm sorry,' said Fari, her eyes taking in her feet. An Indian modesty.

The idea of the stars was appealing, but not with him. He seemed to be the type of man who would prefer to look at her waist than the stars. Plus, he was short. She didn't trust short, well-fed men. Not that she had met many. No, she would wait until all the fat men had their brandy and slept before she took in the heavens, alone.

The whole world was asleep when Fari stepped out onto the deck.

Now, she looks up to the sky from her solitary place at the stern and takes a slow breath in, shaking her head with amazement. The sliver of crescent moon has allowed the Milky Way to shine so brightly it seems God has laid out the stars just for her; the sky an incredible wash of white glitter that makes every moment of her life seem pointless, and crucial, together.

The salty breeze picks up a little and Fari wraps her sari around her shoulders, and up over her head like a hood, unable to take her eyes off the shimmering sky. After Neymat was killed, she had been more adrift than she was here on the ocean. She questioned her future, her hopes, her dreams. Nothing was the same without him. *Hum Dono*. Now, here in the midnight path of heaven, she casts up his favourite prayer:

Oh God! Refresh and gladden my spirit. Purify my heart. Illumine my powers. I lay all my affairs in Thy hand. Thou art my Guide and my Refuge. I will no longer be sorrowful and grieved; I will be a happy and joyful being. Oh God! I will no longer be full of anxiety, nor will I let trouble harass me. I will not dwell on the unpleasant things of life.

Oh God! Thou art more friend to me than I am to myself.

I dedicate myself to Thee, Oh Lord.

When she opens her eyes, they are drawn sharply downwards, because the stars have fallen into the sea.

The churning white froth and spray under the stern has turned neon blue, and the ocean surrounding the boat sparkles with a million tiny lights, jumping and swirling, lighting up the trail of the ship. Stunned, Fari leans over the railing, wide-eyed and white-knuckled, her plait swinging, her sari-hood billowing like a sail. The phosphorescence seems an otherworldly magic, a field of heavenly light. Is it for her? Is this sorcery or is it God? A warmth spreads through her chest and down to her bare toes on the carpeted deck. She looks around, up and down, but there isn't a soul to see it, not a single witness to the glowing message that allows her heavy heart, finally, to breathe.

'It's him . . .' she whispers smiling, and her voice is carried away by the salt and the sea wind.

1967. Adelaide.

'Missus Daisy, let me help you.'

Fari approaches the wispy and frail old woman who is struggling to pull herself up out of a chair in the rec room.

'No. I can do it. You just leave me,' Daisy Butler says, exercising her sharp tongue. She pushes her palms into the armrests and flaps her elbows like a crow in an attempt to launch herself upwards.

Fari works at Our Lady Immaculate aged care facility, four days a week. She cleans and tidies. She helps the residents go to the bathroom. She brushes their hair, dresses the ladies, and keeps spirits up by chatting to them about India, her schooling, and the boat ride across the sea.

'Here, put your arm around my shoulder,' Fari says, leaning down to take Mrs Butler's hand.

'Don't you touch me!' Daisy squawks. 'How do I know where you've been? You keep your hands to yourself. Where's Eileen?'

'Eileen doesn't work today, Missus Daisy. You have me.'

'I don't want you. You're dirty.'

'I am as clean as a new pin. I promise. I took a soapy bath before work this morning,' Fari says, with a smile to Mr Harrington.

He chuckles from the lounge. 'Daisy, don't be so bloomin' stubborn.'

The old woman sits back, folds her crinkled arms, presses her stockinged knees together firmly, and sets her jaw like glue.

Daisy Butler used to be beautiful. When she was nineteen, she moved from Sydney's Newport to South Australia to marry Harry James Butler, Adelaide's finest young banker. She met him at a party her parents had given, at the Royal Prince Alfred Yacht Club on Pittwater. Harry looked well in a tuxedo. Moving to Adelaide with him was an easy choice. She spent a wonderful sixty-five years as his wife, gardening, cooking, sewing her own frocks and playing the piano. Her life had been a lark.

But now she can do none of those things. Harry is long dead, and her ocean-blue eyes have turned glaucoma grey. Her two daughters, Holly and Felicity, have their own lives, back on the North Shore of Sydney. They have their own children, their own parties and friends. She doesn't see them, really. Adelaide is so far away.

Fari can see that she is lonely, that she has closed the book of her life and is simply waiting to die.

'All right, madam,' Fari says to Daisy, pulling a cloth from the pocket of her royal-blue pinafore and dusting the side board. 'You stay there. I've plenty to keep me busy. You tell me if you change your mind.'

The SS *Oronsay* arrived in Adelaide on Australia Day. Tiny coloured flags were strung between the ornate facades of the limestone colonial buildings on Rundle Street. The January heat of the south coast was gentle and dry, and blown away every so often by a gust of ocean breeze. Khodi had come to meet his mother and sisters at the port, and taken them back to his home, to Joan. He stood like a beautiful bronzed statue on the dock, waving and smiling so broadly they could see his white teeth from the ship. Dolly had embraced him like air.

They walked down Rundle Street and took in the sights. Fari wondered why there were so few people about. This was a day of celebration in this country! The streets should be full. In India she wouldn't be able to take three steps without rubbing shoulders with someone.

'Khodi, what's happened? Has somebody important died here?' Fari asked her brother as they took in a small afternoon tea of sandwiches and iced biscuits, in the centre of downtown Adelaide. 'Is the country in mourning?'

'Fari-jaan, nothing has happened. This is Australia! Big and clean, like I said.'

'But . . .' she said, glancing around at the tidy cafe, the neat rows of tables, the peaceful street, 'where have all the people gone?'

Khodi laughed and kissed her cheeks, 'Oh I missed you, my Fari. This is it, jaanam. There aren't any more people,' he said, smiling.

They arrived at the house to a warm welcome. Joan had made up the spare room in their tidy brick house for Dolly, Mona and her children, and the sleepout for Fari. She was effusive in her apologies that she did not have more rooms to offer. Fari had a single bed to herself, made up with a crocheted coverlet and lace pillows, a small bedside table with an electric lamp, and a little clock. She put her small suitcase at the foot of the bed, took off her sandals, and stood to pray. The air was different here, like God had taken all the water out of it. The sky was wide, the space overwhelming. When you looked out of the window of the house, it was like looking out a porthole to the sea – the land stretching on forever.

That night, Fari tried to sleep on the plush bed, but with only the buzz of insects outside the open window to fill the air, she couldn't. Fari had never slept in a room by herself. For twenty-five years there had always been a body next to her, the sound of breathing, a light snore, an occasional cough or giggle or murmur. For the first time, she was scared of the dark.

Careful not to disturb the house, she tiptoed to Mona and Dolly's room, covered Nabil with the sheet he had kicked off, scooped up Soosun, and carried her back to the sleepout. Snuggling the little girl tightly, Fari finally found rest.

The next day, Khodi took them all to a shopping centre, and taught them how to shop for groceries, and more importantly, how to ride the escalator. At first, Fari refused to get on, thinking she would be thrown off at the top, but Khodi grabbed her arm and pulled her on, laughing at her protests. The kids went up and down while the women ate ice-cream and hot chips with tomato sauce.

Joan had stayed home, to prepare the dinner. She was a gracious hostess, and her manners were impeccable, but they were misunderstood and sometimes taken for coolness by her sisters-in-law. To women who were used to communal living and sharing cups of tea and blankets, her reserve felt like aloofness. They weren't sure of her favour, but Khodi seemed to dote on her. The girls tried their best to play along.

At five that evening, while it was still light out, Joan served Dolly, Mona and Fari roast beef, gravy, mashed potatoes, carrots and peas at her well-set table in the dining room.

'Khodi, is this afternoon tea?' asked Fari, in Hindi, smiling, not wanting to offend.

'No, this is dinner, Fari. In Australia they eat dinner at five o'clock.'

After a valiant attempt to eat more food than they could stomach, the women tried to help Joan clear the plates and wash up, but she insisted they 'sit and relax in the living room' since they were 'guests'.

Was this how white women worked? Alone? thought Fari, sending Mona her raised brows. Mona shrugged, quite pleased to lay back and snooze for a time, her natural inclination to be completely at home anywhere was a gift. Dolly was bewildered, but at least she had baby Jinous to bounce on her knee while she looked at the wallpaper. Paisley, like a sari. She had fed the bub on her lap at dinner, by hand, mushing the peas into the potato on her plate and pinching the mix into a small ball to pop into the little girl's mouth. Jinous opened up on cue, like a sparrow, and smacked the cream tablecloth happily with an outstretched hand. Joan had offered Dolly a spoon to feed the baby, but she smiled and pretended not to understand. She had raised five children of her own, and seven of her sister's. Scooping a pat of food into a baby's mouth with her fingers was as natural as breathing.

Without anything to do after dinner, Fari took the older children outside into the garden to play. There was a large centre lawn, neatly clipped, with a white fence surrounding. Pink summer azaleas grew in bushy clumps on the edges. In the middle of the yard, a little concrete path led to a merry-go-round!

'Jaanams! Dekho! You want to have a turn? Chalo, chalo! I'll lift you up,' exclaimed Fari as the kids came running after her, shoeless down the path.

Hearing the cries of excitement and joy, Khodi came outside to find four children dangling, red-faced, from the Hills hoist clothesline, squealing wildly and swinging their legs as Fari turned it around and around, her plait flying in the air.

The women soon realised that they were most definitely 'guests' and that Khodi and Joan's house was just a temporary place to lodge until they found a home of their own. It was Joan who got Fari the job at Our Lady Immaculate, and patiently explained to her what 'aged care' was, for she had never heard of such a thing. In India, the 'aged' are cared for in the same way babies are, by their families. Fari thought the idea of a special home just for old people absurd – 'Where are their children? Dead?' – but Khodi explained, 'It's not like that here, Fari-jaan. People live separately. Families don't rely on one another to cope.' He was happy she was going to work with the elderly. She would be a terrific nurse, all warmth and cheer and care. Mona took a job as a cleaner at a nearby hotel.

Khodi often disappeared in the afternoons, to go swimming at Glenelg Beach. He took Fari once or twice, but she couldn't swim, and was terrified of the endlessness of the ocean. Khodi had always loved water. When he was a little boy in Persia, he would swim in the frozen river, his grandfather helping him to break the ice. Now, Fari watched her brother strike out into the blue while she sat on the white sand, pouring it through her fingers. Khodi wasn't a fast swimmer, but he was determined. He liked to swim breaststroke underwater for as long as he could before surfacing to breathe quickly and dive down again.

In the silent vastness of the ocean, the cold water rushing past his face, strong legs opening and closing in his wake, Khodi felt closer to God than anywhere else on earth.

'Daisy, Daisy, give me your answer do . . .' Fari sings softly, as if to herself, secretly eyeing Daisy Butler, who is still struggling to get up out of her chair. 'I'm half crazy, over the love of you,' she goes on, louder, with a Hindi lilt, winking at Mr Harrington. They both know Daisy can hear her singing.

He takes up the game. 'It won't be a fancy marriage . . .' he croons in a croaky baritone, 'I can't afford a carriage . . .'

Together, he and Fari sing to one another, 'But you'll look sweet, upon the seat of a bicycle built for two!'

George Harrington smiles, scratches his chin and begins the next verse while Fari dusts the top of the rec room television, humming along.

'How do you know that song?' Daisy Butler asks tersely, once George is done showing off.

'I know a lot of British songs. I learnt them at my boarding school, when I wasn't busy making sure I was very, very clean,' Fari looks her in the eye and holds her gaze just a second longer than she should. 'But,' she says, going back to her dusting, 'I'd never met anyone called Daisy until I met you, Missus Daisy. Even though in India there are plenty of bicycles built for two.'

Daisy grimaces, but something shifts in her. This is Fari's greatest gift. She can shift anyone.

'Stop talking and help me up,' Daisy says, holding out her withered arm.

Eleven months ago.

I'm at the Playhouse theatre in South Brisbane. I've got a wonderful seat at the front of the balcony. The house is live and every chair sold. People chatter and sip the wine they decanted into plastic cups in the foyer.

I'm not bothered by sitting alone. I like it. In fact, sometimes I prefer it because I can pore over the program, obsessing over the actor bios, the plays they've been in, the choice of headshot. His is steely, brooding. It doesn't really look like him. I wonder if the actors are anything like the characters they play. I try to guess who is sleeping with the director and who is stoked just to have a job, who is doing a pre-show line of coke in the dressing room, who is praying to a guru. But tonight, all I can think about is what I will say when I meet Anthony at the stage door.

We've been texting each other since the kiss, and I casually suggested coming to see his play. He casually suggested a drink afterwards. I accepted. Casually. We sent pithy one-liners back and forth. I laughed out loud at some of his texts. We flirted a bit. And now, to my great shame, my concern is not the integrity of the play or the quality of his acting or where we will sup afterwards, but if he will think I'm cool. This leads to thinking about whether I am, in fact, cool, followed by the sobering conclusion that I am definitely not, because cool people, especially cool people who are grown adults, don't sit about wondering if they're cool, Sita, you idiot.

I clear my throat and adjust my skirt. My legs are too long, always an awkward fit at the theatre. I cross them, careful not to kick the woman on my left. She's wearing a kaftan. The crowd crackles, vibing on the pre-show soundtrack of eighties Aussie rock. The bloke on my right can't help himself and starts busting out the chorus of 'Flame Trees'. His wife leans over, her wine tipping, 'Can't take him anywhere!'

What if I don't like the play? This is unlikely – it's been a huge hit. Anthony is playing two roles. He has casually downplayed his profession as 'doing some pretending', but now, as I read through his program notes, eyebrows up, I see he went to NIDA, has several Arthur Millers under his belt, two Tennessee Williams, Pinter, Chekhov, Ibsen, Shakespeare. Musicals, too, and television. Films.

I begin to shrink. What have I done with my life other than have kids, get divorced and teach high school? I know that these are not small things, I do. I'm not downplaying the importance of being a parent, or marriage, or the nobility of the teaching profession. When I held my babies in my arms for the first time, I felt how I imagine Moses felt when he put his arms out and parted the Red Sea – fucking astonished. And they continue to astonish me, my children. And despite being averse to ever getting married again, I'm not anti-marriage. Devoting your life to the person you love? Choosing them over all others? Vowing to one another and swapping golden rings? It's romantic beyond belief, and I'm a sucker for romance. But truth be told, I feel about marriage the way I feel about tattoos – one is enough, and preferably one that doesn't make people stare. As for teaching, some of the greatest, most intelligent, selfless and funny people I know are teachers. But, there is not a single one who does not spend the last two weeks of term three and most of term four wondering if there is anything else they can do with a teaching degree other than teach. Luckily for your children, by the time term one rolls around, we've all concluded, there isn't. The whole thing is just so . . . scheduled. It's like my pregnant friend, Trace, said this morning as I passed her in the stairwell: 'I need a job where I don't have to wait for a bell to ring before I can pee.'

Motherhood, marriage, teaching – they are wonderful things. But they're just not how I see myself, or how I feel on the inside. They're roles. I put on the costume. I play my part. Sometimes I play it well, and sometimes I wonder if I've fooled anyone at all.

Truthfully, I've always felt like an artist – a storyteller – a writer. I'm not a writer. I've written one thing, a short story that was published in a compilation. It's hardly of note. And sometimes, when I see other artists doing what they do, my stomach catches. I get jealous and despondent wondering what my life could have been if I hadn't been so good. If I had said no to marriage, and no to teaching, and yes to things that made no money and went nowhere, but brought me alive.

I close the program and fumble with my packet of Skittles. Mercifully, the lights go down, seat 16 stops singing, the show starts.

As with everything, the book is better. I don't love the play as much as everyone around me seems to. Clapping, cheering, gushing, giggling. I just sit there wondering about him. I chew my lip. I pick at my thumbnail. His talent is obvious. When he is on the stage, I can't look anywhere else. Not because of the lines, but because of what he puts between them.

When the curtain comes down, I clap slowly amid the furore. I text Andy:

This is a disaster.

Buzz.

What?! Why? It's had such rave reviews!

Not the show. Him.

Buzz.

Oh no. Was he awful?

Worse . . . he was brilliant.

Buzz.

Oh yeah, that's terrible. Dump him now. Find a shitty actor to date.

I'm serious! I should've worn black.

I'm in a boho frock with a plunging neck, and my favourite coat, a mulberry-coloured faux fur. I feel overdone. Unsophisticated. I've tried far too hard. Someone who commits the kind of blue-chip, magnificent fraud I just witnessed onstage will see through me the second I step out of the theatre.

Buzz.

Do. Not. Overthink. This. I swear to God, Seets. Put your phone away and just enjoy the moment.

Buzz.

Meet you at the stage door?

It's him.

Sure. You were really wonderful! I text quickly.

Buzz.

Too kind. I'll just take a quick shower. Be out in 10.

You were really wonderful, *exclamation mark*? Hopeless. Earnest, rainbow Paddle Pop fool.

I chew the inside of my cheek as I lean against the wall of the tunnel between the two theatres. Anthony appears at the stage door, rubbing the back of his neck, eyes scanning. If he sees me he doesn't show it. I watch him make his way through the milling crowd. He kisses a tall man, a fellow actor, and clasps his forearm. He squeezes the hand of a woman in black jeans and boots and says something I can't hear. The crowd's titter echoes in the tunnel. The handsome young boy who played the lead is surrounded by adoring girls with programs. Anthony meets his eye and gives him a raised-arm goodbye, rolling his shoulder, wincing slightly. A cool draught blows down the tunnel from the street and catches my hair, carrying the voices of the crowd to the river. And then he's there, rubbing his chin stubble, smiling sincerely, embracing me with ease.

'It's great to see you,' he says, kissing my cheek warmly, 'I'm excited you're here.' No hint of guile. The country boy for a minute.

'My pleasure.' Nerves taken in the breeze. 'It's not every day you get to see your Bumble date die a horrific, bloody death.'

Anthony gives a wry smile, regarding me with the blue-grey. 'Sita. That is a bangin' coat.'

2020. Toowoomba.

I push the papers across the front desk of the courthouse, towards a thin, grey man with a striped polo shirt and protruding nose hair. He thumbs through them officiously and asks, 'I suppose the dates are in here somewhere, but has it been more than a year since?'

'Yes, it has.'

'Well, you'll have to swear.'

'I beg your pardon?'

'You'll have to swear on the Bible, if you're a Christian. Pop your hand on here,' he says, tapping the top of a black, leather Bible with gold inlay. This is assumptive tapping. He thinks I'm Christian. Do I look Christian? Or does he expect most people who walk through the doors of the Toowoomba court-house are Christian?

I look at his white badge: Keith Tomlinson, Justice of the Peace. I clear my throat gently. 'I'm not Christian.'

'You can still swear on the Bible. It doesn't matter.'

I kind of think it does, Keith.

I may be utterly Godless right now, but I spent every Sunday of my childhood learning about religion. It was very important to my family that I knew about all faiths, not just my own. Christians, Jews, Muslims, Buddhists, Hindus, Zoroastrians – I could tell you about their gods and their laws. I could speak eloquently about the difference between Shia and Sunni Islam, about confession and communion, about Brahma, Vishnu and Shiva, and about Zoroastrian water ritual and fire worship. I could give Keith my take on the noble eightfold path, the dualistic cosmology of good and evil, and a metaphorical interpretation of the Holy Trinity that would get him thrown out of church on Sunday, and I could definitely inform him that, actually, if he were to heed what Jesus said in Matthew 5:33–37: 'But I say to you, Do not take an oath at all, either by heaven, for it is the throne of God, or by the earth, for it is his footstool, or by Jerusalem, for it is the city of the great King. And do not take an oath by your head, for you cannot make one hair white or black. Let what you say be simply "Yes" or "No"; anything more than this comes from evil,' then perhaps he wouldn't be so cavalier about all this oathing, anyway.

But, I don't. Instead, I quietly ask, 'Is there another option?'

'You can say this affirmation,' Keith concedes, pointing to a bit of tattered A4 sticky taped to the corner of the desk, edges curling.

I read the words out loud: 'I solemnly, sincerely and truly affirm and declare that the contents of this document are true and correct to the best of my knowledge.'

'Very good,' says Keith. A mild display of bureaucratic encouragement. 'Now, sign here.'

I pick up the black plastic Bic and sign my name to the papers that say that my fifteen-year marriage is officially over. I put the pen down and hear it land with a rattle on the desk. I hear a chair scrape behind me and a lady entering the courthouse slip her umbrella into a plastic sleeve. I hear the rain washing through the gutters on the street, and under the wheels of fast-moving cars. I hear the plastic fingernails of the administrator sitting in the booth next to Keith, clipping her keyboard. My mouth goes dry.

'It's my turn,' Keith says, kindly taking back the papers I have Godlessly oathed to be true, and signing them without ceremony. His red stamp lands on the paper and I feel a sting as I swallow.

'There!' he says, pushing the lot back across the desk, his nose hairs quivering above his taut smile. 'Now, that was easy, wasn't it?'

1967. Sydney.

John took up the tea his mother had poured. 'How do you feel about Fari, Mum?'

Now that John and his sister had left home, Margaret had taken up a post as the eagle-eyed matron of Aspinall House, at

Scots College, a boarding school in the exclusive, harbourside suburb of Bellevue Hill. John had brought Fari up to meet her. Margaret had been polite, and welcoming, and farewelled her graciously when she left.

'I would like your consent to marry her,' John said.

'I don't really know her very well,' Margaret said, ever the pragmatist.

'We can arrange for you to get to know her better, assuming that you would get to know her as an individual, regardless of her colour and her race. Would you give your consent then, if you were happy with her as an individual?'

Margaret poured her own tea. 'It's really none of my business. It's up to you. You're old enough to make your own decisions, John.'

'I need your consent, Mum. I've explained why. Bahá'ís cannot marry without the consent of both their parents.'

'Well, I don't want to give it,' Margaret said curtly, taking up a lemon crisp and bringing her china cup to her lips.

'Does that mean you're going to deprive me from getting married for the rest of my life? I'll be the end of the line, then. You'll have no grandchildren, because I'll never get married without your consent, as long as you're alive.'

Margaret was torn. Life had not turned in the ways she expected it to. When John told her he was converting to the Bahá'í faith, she had cut him off financially, and removed his name from her will. Yet, he had flourished. He had educated himself, had a well-paid job, was well liked and respected in the community, and had travelled the world with money to spare. Despite herself, she was proud of him. Now, he brings home an Indian lady to meet her. Fari was lovely. Actually, she thought her quite genteel. But what would people think of it? What would they think of her grandchildren? Still, it was better to have grandchildren whose parents were unusual, than not to have them at all. Her son came by his stubbornness honestly, she thought.

'All right,' she said with a sigh. 'I will give you my consent, John. But I'm not coming to the wedding.'

'Well that would be very sad, Mum,' said John. 'But, that's up to you.'

John and Fari were married on a bright day in December that year. John looked like Buddy Holly in his suit and dark, square glasses. Fari looked like a jasmine in bloom, delicate flowers embroidered on her white sari with silver thread. As they took their vows, Dolly smiled. She looked over at Margaret – delicately perched in the front row, in a box hat and shot-silk jacket, and perfectly polished shoes. She had tears falling down her cheeks.

1968. The Bruce Highway. South of Townsville.

Fari was seven months pregnant in the passenger seat of a Ford Falcon when she heard that Khodi was missing. For hours, John had been wrestling with how to tell her, and now they were nearing Townsville, their new home, he knew he couldn't put it off any longer.

'Darling, I have to tell you something,' he said gently. 'It's about Khodi.'

'Khodi? What is it?'

'He's missing, sweetheart. He went swimming last night, in the ocean. He said he felt unwell and he wanted to go for a swim, but he never came back home.'

'Khodi is missing?'

'They found his things on the jetty – shoes and shirt. Joan says the police are looking. Everyone is out looking, darling.'

Fari sat staring straight ahead, her mind struggling with everything her husband had just said. She thought of the ocean at Glenelg, the vastness, the rocks, the sand. Why was he feeling sick? Why would he swim at night-time? 'Sadie the Cleaning Lady' started playing on the tinny car radio. Last year, Prime Minister Harold Holt went swimming at Cheviot Beach off the choppy coast of Victoria and never returned. Presumably, he was swallowed up by Bass Strait while the country searched for clues and tore open the bellies of sharks. They never found his body.

Fari thought about her brother. He was the closest thing to a father she had. Her hand gripped the handle of the car door. She began to sweat, her thoughts coming like bullets. Oh Khodi, Khodi! You can't be eaten by whales or ripped apart by beasts! You can't be gone! God wouldn't take a man like that and swallow him up without leaving even a morsel, would he?

Maybe he would. Maybe Khodi was worth taking whole.

It was Khodi who had given her permission to marry. Khodi who she had gone to and said, 'This Australian man, John, he sat next to me on the bus, he came to dinner with us, and he wants to take me sight-seeing tomorrow – alone. Khodi, what should I do?'

'Fari,' Khodi had said, putting his hand over hers, 'he is a very good man, a good Bahá'í. Everyone respects him. Go with him, and if he asks you to marry him, say yes.'

'All right,' she had said, but her breath had caught on it.

Khodi was reassuring as ever. 'Fari-jaan, he will be good to you. He will look after you and you'll never need to worry, my jaan.'

But now, she was worried. She prayed:

Oh God, guide him, protect him, make of him a shining lamp and a brilliant star. Thou art the mighty and the powerful!

Oh God, guide him, protect him, make of him a shining lamp and a brilliant star. Thou art the mighty and the powerful!

Oh God, guide him, protect him, make of him a shining lamp and a brilliant star. Thou art the mighty and the powerful!

The cane fields of the far north sped by, the sun high in the sky. The baby kicked and squirmed, feeling a change in the womb, blood churning.

Two thousand kilometres away, on the shores of the St Vincent Gulf, Khodi's swollen body washed up on the beach. Whole, but utterly lifeless.

Fari put a hand to her belly, 'Stop the car, John-John, I'm going to be sick.'

2016. Brisbane.

'Sita, what about the children, darling? Have you told the children?'

'Yes, Dad, we have,' I say. Flatly now, resigned.

It's 2pm. I've managed to drag myself out of bed. We're on the back deck overlooking the banana trees and dragon fruit vines growing on the timber fence of the house next door. Two blue-faced honeyeaters are beak-deep in a banana blossom. I'm laid back on a leather couch that we paid a fortune for, but is now faded and a bit beaten down, like us. Sadness is covering me like a blanket. My eyes are heavy and swollen, my face sensitive to the touch, but I'm warm with it. My mind is so tired I'm incapable of dire thoughts. I feel like I'm under the influence of several glasses of scotch, but I've not had a drop. Dad has sorted out the Medicare, driven me to the transport department to begin the process of changing my name, and spoken at length about cars and houses, furniture and other practicalities. Now he is on the phone to my brother, pacing the deck, stepping over toys and pet bowls, speaking in hushed tones in the way men do when something important and sensitive needs to be 'dealt with'. I secretly adore them for it. The feeling of being looked after, having my bag of troubles picked up and tossed between my father and brother for a few moments, both of them feeling the weight, the girth, deciding if they should unpack it or burn it or bury it in a field. List making, strategising. I know in my heart this is all just theatrics. I'm watching a play of my life. I will watch them pass around my troubles, but in the end

I will pick them right back up again, and send everyone home. Show's over, kids. And then, late at night in my bedroom, I will unpack them quietly, one by one. Alone.

Fari has cleaned the entire house, top to bottom. She keeps appearing with things in hand, 'Is this William's or Leo's shirt?' or calling from the kitchen, 'Sita! Where do you keep the dustpan and brush?'

'Ma, relax. Come and sit down,' I call back, empty.

'What is it? You want tea?' she calls. 'I'll fry you a paratha. You want? Or a bikkie? John-John! Will you go to Coles? We need chicken! Sita, butter chicken for the kids, yes? They will eat? What about William? He likes my rice, he can eat rice.'

She bustles out to the deck and hangs several towels over the railing. 'These need sun!'

'Fari,' my dad says, gently capturing her in his arms on the way past. 'Sit down, darling. We can make a shopping list together, and then I'll go to Coles.' He rubs her back in circles as a moment of peace descends. They sit on the deck like two satellites orbiting a dying planet; Dad looking at his phone, Mum nervously picking dead leaves out of the succulent pot on the coffee table, me staring.

After a minute, Fari says, 'What happened, Sita? Tell us.'

I've been waiting for this question. What happened to your marriage? Why, after fifteen years and three children, have you decided to part ways and live in two houses and subject your kids to a life of nomadism? Why don't you love each other anymore? Why aren't you capable of pretending it's all okay for the sake of your children? What has happened that is so awful that you are changing the course of everyone's lives, changing the narrative forever, the story your babies will tell their own babies about how they grew up? What? Happened?

The truth is, I don't know.

Nothing happened. Everything happened.

I loved Borhan. He was my first everything, and I, his. I still love him, in the way you love family. Family who can drive you completely mad, but would give you a kidney if you needed it. I have no choice. We lost our innocence together, Borhan and I. We built our lives on sand. We married when we were twenty years old. The sand shifted and blew, and in all that spinning dust we got the worst of each other – the selfishness of youth, the bumbling ambition, the hurt pride, the passive aggressive silences, the fledgling attempts to transcend all the bullshit and rise above, only to realise the resentment we buried or patted down would always be unearthed in a storm. That everything we believed at nineteen, about God, about love, about sacrifice, about marriage, had been completely upended. Borhan believed our love had irretrievably been lost, and I didn't know what I believed. I was adrift in it, this sea of unbelieving.

But how could I explain this to my mother and father? A couple who lived not for themselves, or for each other, but for God? Who lived for their beliefs, who had unshakeable faith! I was so ashamed at how it would all sound, how trivial, how small. I'd spent so many years trying to be good, trying to sacrifice everything I could for my marriage, my children. Trying to live by a set of principles handed down to me by the most wonderful, noble people I knew, and still I had failed.

'I don't know what happened, Ma,' I said plainly, swallowing the overwhelm that threatened, my eyes holding fast to the decking.

We sat for a moment.

'Okay baby, forget it,' she said suddenly, standing up, closing the discussion that never happened. 'It's finished now.'

'I failed, Ma,' I said, a small sob escaping my throat. 'I feel like I failed everyone.'

'Nonsense. You tried your best, didn't you?' said my dad, with gusto.

'Yes.'

'Well then, you haven't failed, my precious treasure,' he said, reaching his arms across to me, palms out. I put my hands in his. 'But,' his voice was warm and even, 'are you sure about this? Have you both absolutely made up your minds?'

'We have, Dad.'

'Well then, time to get on with it,' he said, ending the discussion about why his youngest daughter's marriage was over by squeezing my hands tightly and standing up, pocketing his notebook and pen neatly, and patting his pocket. 'Chin up. Go pick up your children from school. I'm off to buy Mum's chicken.'

1981. Toowoomba.

The lobby lift doors opened and Nurse Beverly ushered Fari and Dolly quickly inside, Fari breathing and humming low through a strong contraction, her lips pursed tight, her knees bent. Nurse Beverly was firm, speaking to her like she was a small child, 'Breathe, Mrs Walker, and hold it in. Don't push. Hold it. We don't want the baby to come too quickly, do we?'

Dolly breathed deeply in tandem, and held her youngest daughter by the arm, steadying her as the carpeted lift moved upwards. The lift door opened and Fari gave a barely audible moan. As Nurse Beverly ushered her into the closest delivery room, Dolly spoke in Farsi, low and keen, 'I'll wait here for John. You don't listen to her, Fari-jaan. If the baby wants to come, let it come.'

Dolly was seventy years old. She had given birth to five babies, four of whom were still living – Mehri, Mona, Irie and Fari. All together, her daughters had given her fifteen grandchildren. The youngest, sweet Rahnee, was almost ten years old, and Dolly had thought the number of grandchildren who would stand around her grave was set. Fifteen. It was a good number.

For twenty-five years she had travelled from daughter to daughter, city to city, looking after her grandchildren. Each week of her life was spent swaddling and rocking, cooking, cleaning, scooping balls of rice and dahl into little mouths, mopping fevered brows with cold towels, packing school lunches, sewing small frocks and shorts with pockets for shells and pebbles, wiping bottoms, washing and hanging cloth nappies, ironing school uniforms, darning knee patches onto trousers, soaking footy shorts and cricket whites, standing outside the school gates with containers of roughly cut fruit, and walking her grandchildren home, hand-stuffing fruit into their mouths.

She didn't realise how happy she would be when she heard there would be one more. One more baby.

Maybe it would be a boy, and that would be fine. Boys were like fire, a blessing and a protection, and she had seen her grandsons burn and blaze through the world with ambition and pride and warmth and love. But girls. Girls were like water. Running, they gave life, and still they reflected it. A little boy would work her bones and warm her cheeks with kisses, but a little girl would be something to keep her spirit alive forever, to wash away her troubles, to nourish her for the rest of her time on earth. With a girl, she would never be alone.

John flew out of the lift doors to see Dolly waiting in the hall.

'Go in, John,' she said urgently. 'Quickly. You go and see.' John knocked tentatively on the delivery room door, but Dolly pushed it open gently, 'Go!'

He was just in time.

John had never seen a baby being born. Fari had given birth to his other three children in the late sixties and early seventies, when fathers weren't allowed in to watch or hold their wives' hands, when birthing was women's work and babies were cleaned and swaddled and taken to a waiting room to be plopped into the arms of their doting dads while their wives freshened up and put on a spot of lipstick. Now, sweating after the sprint from the car park and the frantic scramble through the hospital, John stood at the end of the hospital bed, a foot taller than anyone else in the room, his eyes alight, like a little boy at the edge of the sea, watching the waves hit the sand for the very first time.

Fari was quiet in birthing. Often, her silence belied her readiness to deliver, which is why several of her babies almost emerged in the back seat of the car, or the hospital lobby. Arching her back and bending her knees, she let out a small hum as the head arrived in a gush, covered with dark hair. Nurse Beverly patted her hand and congratulated her. The midwife held the wobbly little head and said, 'Just one more. One more push, Mrs Walker, and you'll be all done.'

John stood frozen. The world moved around him and sound passed through him as he wondered how anyone could ever deserve to be in the presence of something so powerful and selfless and perfect and grand. As the head emerged, his heart swelled with wonder, with love for his wife, for his family, for his life and everyone in it, and when Beverly put his fourth child – a girl – into his arms, crying and mewling, wrinkled and shaking, covered in white goo and red blood and flecks of purple clot, he held her close, gazing in awe at her screwed up, pruney little face, and said, 'You are the most beautiful thing, the most beautiful, precious thing. You are my precious treasure.'

2017. Brisbane.

I've checked all the windows twice. And the doors. There's a back door off the tiny laundry, a front door, two doors leading to a lattice-covered timber verandah running down the side of The Shack, and windows in every room. The kids' rooms have windows with grilles, but mine doesn't. I've left the outside porch lights on, and the hallway light, the laundry light, a tall lamp in the lounge – all lit. If there was to be a burglary, the perpetrator would be able to find everything they needed, swiftly and simply.

The Shack is my new home. It's a small, cosy post-war cottage, nestled happily on the busiest main road in Tarragindi. This is my first night here, and the kids are finally in bed and asleep. I've checked on them several times, felt their faces with the back of my hand, adjusted their blankets, pushed Leo's rolling little body closer to the wall, kissed William on his soft cheeks and breathed in his boy smells because he never lets me do that when he's awake, tucked Layla's ever-escaping toes back under her sheets.

I'm okay. This is going to be okay.

I've never lived by myself, or been the only parent in the house with the children. Before Borhan, I lived with my parents, then at a college dormitory, then in a uni share house and then back to my parents' home before marrying and moving in with my husband. Apropos, Fari is in a state. She's called me about sixteen times today, checking on me, making sure I'm not scared or lonely. I'm not. There's an independence in all this, and I love not having to consult anyone about kitchen storage, or which couch to buy, whether to rinse before putting the plates in the dishwasher, who will wash the pots. Little discussions that exhaust a marriage. Moving out has already proven that it's much harder work to resent someone for not washing the pots than it is to just wash them yourself.

I grab a slice of pizza from the box on the dining table. I found this table on the footpath outside a house on Laura Street. The people who owned it saw me eyeing it off and offered to drop it over in their ute. It's a hexagon, solid oak, stained dark, with four chunky square chairs. I love it. It's seen things. The seat cushions that were once cream are now stained and frayed, but like all of us, they have potential. Perhaps I'll cover them, I think. I could find out how to do that. My friend Fiona brought me some flowers earlier today, peonies and roses, and they're sitting in a plastic utensil holder in the middle of the hexagon. I can't find my vase.

There are boxes stacked in each room – toys still to unpack, books, clothes, half-full cupboards, coat-hangers strewn about, bits of used packing tape and cut twine, and shoes in the middle of the hallway – some weird snow boots, worn once. A dear friend of mine hung fairy lights on my verandah this morning, and now they glow into the kids' rooms, making The Shack feel like home.

Renting here, in the same suburb as Borhan, was a conscious choice. It's not cheap, and I'm not flush with cash, but I have just enough to get by, and the kids will stay in the neighbourhood, in the community they know and love. I've never really wanted more than a humble sort of existence – my books, my kids, enough spare change to get to the beach occasionally, or the movies. This little cottage with its little yard and its little carport and its little porch suits me. I boil the kettle as I munch cold pizza.

I'm okay, this is all okay.

Look, it may not be okay. On the off chance that it isn't, I've unpacked a baseball bat from the kids' boxes and put it next to my bed. It's a forest-green Easton. Well-chipped, but heavy enough to put a decent dint in something like a human head. Naturally, a glorified stick and my swinging skills as the first line of defence in any home security crisis is completely absurd, a folly in fact, as I would crumple immediately at any intrusion, but Mister Green Bat somehow provides me with the nebulous sort of comfort others get from complete alarm systems or electric fences. Mister Green Bat and I are ready to defend the compound.

There's a soft knock at the door as the kettle clicks off. I jump and tentatively call, 'Who is it?' not wanting to wake the kids.

Another knock, a bit louder this time.

I grab Mister Green Bat, approach the front door and say, in the voice my dad uses to talk to the tax office, 'Who is it?'

'It's Bonnie, dickhead! Open the door.'

I unlatch the chain and the deadbolt and swing open the door and there she is, laden with bags.

'I know this is a terrible time to be bringing more shit into your house, but you will love this,' she says, kissing me on the cheek and swishing past, 'Which one is your room?'

I point her to it. She dumps all the bags onto my bed with a flourish, and turns back to me in the doorway. 'Nice floors!

I've seen a rug that will be perfect in this room. Cute porch, too. Are we having a game of T-ball or are you going to beat me to death with that?'

Bonnie is the type of woman who makes you believe that no matter how old you are, how worried, how weighed down with life's necessities and gripes, you can always and forever be twenty-one and fancy-free with a pair of fantastic shoes and the perfect earrings. She loves clothes and handbags, and she never pays full price for anything. Bonnie has a gift for finding sexy designer pieces at garage sales, the best eyeshadow in the bargain bin at Priceline, and the most perfect, transcendent, glorious shoes hiding behind a pile of cabbage at the Sunday markets. Tonight, she has brought me several bags of beautiful, shiny, lovely things, in an attempt to cheer me – with the added bonus of freeing up her own closet.

'Ooh, pizza!'

Bonnie's kids are allergic to gluten, processed meat, anything with preservatives, strawberries, dairy products and soap.

'Finish it,' I say, handing her the box. 'Cuppa?'

She looks at me and smiles. 'How about we take the pizza out the front instead?'

There is an enormous pale gum tree growing on the front fence-line of The Shack. It has a gap carved out of its foliage for the powerlines to pass through, and beautiful dusty-green leaves. Its small brown gumnuts are scattered all over the path and the front yard. Leo collected handfuls earlier today and has made little piles of them here and there. Little gumnut pyramids in the moonlight. Bonnie and I bounce a handful of them off the trampoline and crawl on. We lie back next to each other, her in exercise tights, me in a sleeveless nightie, and look up through the leaves to the summer stars, the soles of our bare feet catching the night air. Bonnie hands me a cigarette, lighting up her own and passing over the lighter. Together we take slow drags, flicking the ash through the gaps between the springs, watching the smoke curl up into the breezeless night. A possum wanders deftly along the powerline, its curled tail bobbing gently.

'This place suits you.'

'I know. It feels good.'

'Maybe you could live here forever? Cover the place in silk, put in a birdbath, slowly replace the children with cats?'

'All excellent ideas, Bon-Bon,' I say, blank-faced like a Renaissance painting. 'I'm seriously considering filling the kitchen cupboards with books and eating directly from the pots and pans from now on.'

'You must,' she gushes. 'I'll buy you some silver spoons.'

We're on a roll now.

'Did you know that when you no longer have a husband, the kids can just eat toast for dinner?'

'I've heard it said, yes, but sadly I can only dream of such things,' she says with a faraway look. 'Bill wants a pig for Christmas.'

'An actual pig?'

Bonnie rolls over onto her stomach, bouncing us gently, 'It's a barbecue that looks like a pig.'

I love Bill. He's Bonnie's perfect match. He's cool and dry, sexy and sun-worn in the way of wiry country boys from the northern rivers of New South Wales – looks like he grew up eating grass and catching fish with his hands. I'm sure he has taken every hallucinogen he could forage in his time, but he doesn't like us smoking. He tut-tuts and lectures and Bonnie politely asks him to remove his head from his rear and let her live a little, and he doesn't look up, simply sucks air through his teeth and continues to lovingly season the organic pork and braised fennel he's preparing (shoeless, in stubbies) at the hand-hewn wooden counter of their half-renovated kitchen, knowing full well that any man within a hundred kilometres would give their left testicle to be the one cooking pork for Bonnie.

We lie on our sides and finish the pizza, light up another round, listen to the night cicadas, a dog barking, two bats fighting in the gum. The branches above us move like giant tree puppets in the moonlight.

Bonnie stubs out her dart, pulls out a small felt bag and puts it my hand.

'For you, Madame.'

I take the soft parcel, pull the blue drawstring open and feel inside, taking out a ring and holding it up to the moonlight with a little gasp, 'What have you done, Bonita?'

The ring is sterling silver. Hand hammered. Fine and beautiful and one of a kind. Like her.

'I don't know how Bill would feel about us getting married,' I swoon, sitting up and gazing at my wondrous friend.

'He'd love to be rid of me,' she laughs.

'And I'd love to have you. It's the perfect arrangement.'

'Now, you listen to me, Seets.' Bonnie pulls away, takes the ring from me and holds my hands. 'I'd love to marry you. I think you're everything anyone could ever want, you understand? I think you're gorgeous and selfless and funny and full of charm, and I think Borhan is the stupidest man to ever live for losing you, but . . .' she says like a school marm, slipping the silver onto my ring finger, 'I thought perhaps, this time round . . . you should marry yourself.'

I squeeze Bonnie's hand, looking down, swallowing the feelings that are always just there, sitting behind my eyes and under my skin. 'Thanks, Bon. I love it.'

'Chin up, kid. I still think you should find some beautiful, dumb hunk to bonk immediately,' she says, lying back down and taking out the cigs.

I laugh and lay back with her, our knees bent, the trampoline bouncing gently, a car pulling out of the driveway next door, tipsy Friday night voices calling goodbye. The smoke twists up around us.

'Nah,' I say, holding my hand up to the moonlight, 'it's the pirate's life for me.'

And for a moment that passes like a darting swallow, we're twenty-one again.

1938. Tehran.

Dolly feels Khodi's forehead for the hundredth time. It is still burning. She moves her hands down over the sparseness of his little body, to his perfect brown feet, freezing under the grey hospital blanket. Swaddled to her breast is baby Irie, beginning to squeak and squirm for milk, and behind her, in a small steel cot, Mehri and Mona sleep soundly, their black curls covering the mattress. Dolly turns to the window, wearily unbuttons her coat and blouse, and puts Irie to her nipple, the soothing rush of milk calming both her and her baby girl. The concrete hospital room is high up and Iran's capital Tehran is laid out before her, an oasis in the desert. It is a clear, still night and the lights of the city and the thick layer of January snow that covers buildings and trees are mirrored by a full moon. The ancient city of poets and kings glows, but Dolly sees only her pallid reflection in the glass. She is exhausted.

'Dolly, my jaan.'

Thank God. Behmaan is here.

Dolly embraces her tall husband, baby Irie pressed between them as she kisses him three times. One cheek, then the other, then on the mouth, feeling his thick moustache tickle her nose. He holds her face and then the baby's, warmly.

'Where's the doctor?' he asks, moving to Khodi and sitting next to his son on the bed, kissing his cheeks and holding his limp hands. The boy doesn't stir, just breathes in catching starts, with his mouth open like a sleeping mouse.

'They said he's coming.'

Khodi had been burning up for five days, and coughing for seven before that. The treatments weren't making any difference, and even though he was receiving fluids through a drip, he was becoming thinner and paler by the hour, his cheeks ashen. He was the brightest boy before he took ill – sweet and sunny and without complaint or fear; his sisters' plaything, his father's joy. Dolly laid her hopes at his feet like a wreath of flowers. In this land of men and mountains, having allies was important. Having a strong and good son was a blessing that might one day save her life or her daughters' lives. But now he lay dying, her only son, her boy, her Rajah.

Doctor Ghafari was an excellent physician. He was balding and rotund and he sweated like a seal in the desert, but he had married many souls with bodies other doctors had all but tagged for the morgue. Some said that this was because his faith in Allah was unparalleled, and some said it was because his mother had prayed at the feet of the Alborz for a saint. Ghafari himself was famous for praying before each diagnosis, and after each treatment.

'Mr and Mrs Rahpayma, a pleasure to see you again. Please, don't get up, please. Sit.'

The doctor gave his prognosis calmly, and with his usual poetry: 'We have done everything we can for Khodi, sweet boy, may Allah protect him. Now, we are at a fork in the road, and only God can choose his path. If your son makes it through this night, he will be yours. If not . . .' he said gently, wiping the sweat from his brow, 'he will be God's.'

At 3am Dolly woke with a start. Behmaan was dozing in a chair, his head leaning against the wall. She quickly felt for her son's breath. He was still alive, thank God. Shivering, but alive. She covered his shoulders, left the bed and gently shook her husband awake, 'Behmaan, Behmaan, wake up,' she whispered. 'I had a dream.'

In Dolly's dream, the toddler was standing all alone in the middle of a square, white room. All of a sudden, the room began filling up with creatures. Thick black centipedes crawled under the doorway, and beetles emerged from the walls. Red and brown snakes slithered in the windows, along with hornets, flying and buzzing sharply, encircling the little boy. Brown desert scorpions clicked fiercely as they inched towards him, but Khodi stood still, his face unmoved, watching the wicked, poisonous barbs and fangs getting closer and closer. Just as the beasts were about to commence the feast, Dolly burst through the window of the room, flying as though she had wings, her feet lifted off the ground. She swept Khodi up into her arms and flew back out into the clear air, like an eagle. She flew and flew, over the mountains, and then low, low over the sand, holding her small son tightly in her arms, kissing his hair, and squeezing his warm body tightly.

'This dream is very good,' said her husband with a broad, sleepy smile, taking her hand in his.

'It is the very best dream,' Dolly sighed, relief on her breath as she lay back down next to her son and rolled a squeaking Irie onto her breast, once again. 'He will live.'

'Inshallah,' said Behmaan, closing his eyes. If God wills.

At 5am Khodi began to sweat and toss, turning towards his mother and baby sister, his warm foot kicking the blanket away. Outside, the sun rose over the snowy Alborz Mountains, bathing Tehran in morning light.

1945. Tehran.

Mehri saw her mother shift. She was aware of Dolly in a way special to eldest daughters. Her movements, her moods, a rub of the neck, a raised brow, the way her voice changed slightly when she was happy, or tired, or upset. Dolly was sewing a collar on a man's work shirt, making swift movements with the needle and white thread. Usually she chatted, or hummed, or gave instructions on how many potatoes to peel or how much chilli to use, but today she was silent and far away. Mehri didn't like it.

The war had taken plenty from Dolly, but it had taken from everyone. The Soviets and the British had occupied Iran, using it as a trade route for their battle against the Nazis, plundering it for oil, taking control of the rail network and private trucking, disrupting food distribution chains that left much of the country without grain – hungry and sick and tired. The Persians were no strangers to conflict, and poetic about sufferance, but God knows they had enough of their own wars to fight, without becoming pawns in somebody else's.

In the early stages of the war, Behmaan had contracted tuberculosis, which had become steadily worse, and for the last nine months of 1944, he had been confined to a hospital bed on strict rations, losing weight and coughing up bloody spittle. His business partner had kept their small shop running. It was struggling, but not closed – yet. Dolly and her children lived in what was once the house of the uncle of the Bahá'í Prophet, Baha'u'llah. Dolly and her family were caretaking for the Local Spiritual Assembly of the Bahá'ís of Tehran, keeping the place a secret from the Islamic authorities who would surely bulldoze the historical home if they knew how important it was to the Bahá'ís, to their history.

While her rent was paid in exchange for care of the house, it wasn't enough. Dolly spent her days sewing and cleaning for well-off families to earn money to feed her five children. Every evening she took a humble dinner to her husband in the hospital, herbed rice with broad beans – sabzi-polo, and perhaps a boiled egg. He couldn't get strong on the rations the nurses provided. It wasn't enough, and he always saved his daily bread roll for one of his children.

Behmaan became thinner and thinner, and Dolly began taking Mehri to the hospital with her. The twelve-year-old loved her father. She was his favourite, his sweet jewel. For the first time, Dolly admitted to herself that she may not have him for much longer. He died that spring. When Mehri came home from school to see her Maman rocking and crying in the corner of the family room, she threw her satchel on the ground and fell down wailing and weeping herself.

They buried him on a clear day, under an Afghan pine and near white clay, with the Gulf winds blowing Dolly's dark hair away from her face. For the next twelve months, her prayerful stoicism was punctuated with bouts of extraordinary grief, burning rage, and deep, silent despondence. She tried to hide all of this from her children, but Mehri could see it eating away at her mother like an insidious worm ploughing its way through an apple.

All day, Dolly had been performing household tasks with intractable determination, using them as weapons in the war against her mind. But like all soldiers who fought with fear as their sword, she was losing the battle. With a grimace, she put down the shirt collar and needle, and put on her coat and boots. 'Keshwar-jaan, I'm going out. I won't be long,' Dolly called to her mother-in-law, grabbing her bag and moving swiftly out the door before anyone could ask questions. Very soon, the sun would begin lowering itself onto the horizon, bleeding orange as it went. She needed to hurry.

Mehri waited until the door had closed before she leapt up and followed suit, hissing to Mona, 'Feed Fari and Irie their dinner. I have to go with Maman.' She followed Dolly silently, in soft shoes, staying several metres behind and out of sight. Dolly walked at pace between the square, stone houses, and through dusty lanes, sometimes breaking into a run, her heart beating in her chest like a tombak drum. Mehri followed as quickly and as quietly as she could, under the rows of flapping laundry strung between buildings above. An owl keeping her eyes on a mouse.

Dolly reached the gates of the Doulab Cemetery just as the sun began to lay its skirts on the horizon. The first star of the night gave off a baby-faced glow. Mehri stayed hidden behind a stone wall as her mother paused to watch an elderly gentleman make his way out of the cemetery gates. The man nodded politely as he passed. Dolly wound her way through the tombstones and plaques, heading towards the Afghan pine. A pair of brown sparrows chirruped and hopped in her wake, announcing their presence in the turn of the late afternoon. Sweating, she knelt at the grave of her husband and stared at it as if it were her lover's face, brushing the sand and pine needles away from his plot like she was dusting a mirror, murmuring, 'Kojah raftee, jaan-e-man? Kojah?' Where did you go, my love? Where?

Mehri edged closer, hiding her slight body behind monuments and shrubs, trying to avoid gravel and the tell-tale crunch of dried leaves. She saw her mother clean and dust the headstone, several times, before pausing to pick something up from the bed of a nearby grave.

Dolly turned the small white stone over in her fingers, closing it into her palm and feeling its sharp edges press against her flesh, hoping it would draw blood. Frantically, she reached out and grabbed a handful of them, filling her woollen coat pockets, crawling and scrambling in the dusty grass for more and more. Mehri watched, wide-eyed, from behind the trunk of a thick elm. When her pockets were overflowing with limestone, Dolly stood up wildly. Wiping her wet face with the back of her rock-filled hand, she hurled them one by one at her husband's grave, pelting rocks as hard as she could at the headstone and the grass that covered her love, her arms shaking, her chest heaving with sobs, until her pockets were empty and her fingers red, then she raged and beat her fist against her cheek, turning it pink, a flurry of dry grass and dirt and pine needles and desert dust in her skirts. 'Tanoh hastam!' she cried over and over and over again, sinking to her knees. 'Tanoh hastam! Tanoh! Tanoh!'

I am all alone. Alone. Alone.

Mehri ran out from behind the elm and threw herself at the ground, wrapping her thin arms around Dolly's neck and kissing her cheeks, pulling her dishevelled and sobbing mother into her small chest with balled fists. Dolly leant in, surprised and shaking and gasping into her daughter's worn coat.

Mehri opened her fists to grip the back of her mother tightly. 'Man injaham. Tanoh nabashee. Maroh daree, maroh daree,' she said, strong and firm, in the voice of a woman.

I'm here. You are not alone. You have me, you have me.

Mehri squeezed Dolly as hard as she could, until she felt her mother's breath steady and her shoulders slump. Around them, twilight began its songs of love, the fall of a star in every bird's throat, the sound of black night on the breeze. With a deep breath, Dolly pulled back from her daughter and took her skinny arms in both her hands. She looked into Mehri's eyes. There was her husband's straight gaze. Unafraid. He was also there in her chin, his striking loyalty holding fast to her jaw. Dolly wiped her face with her sleeve and smiled at her eldest daughter. She turned to the ground beside them, looked at the rock-scattered grave of her life's love and said, 'Bosheh jaan-e-man. Man fameedam.' Okay, my darling. I see.

Then she put her anger down in the dust, and together, they walked home.

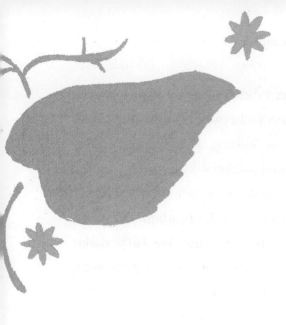

Eleven months ago.

Anthony and I have finished our drinks at The Charming Squire, a pub across the road from the theatre. He's been funny and I've been clever, both of us trying to make the other feel lucky. I suggest an ice-cream, to tease the evening out a bit longer and get us out of the city. We make our way down Melbourne Street, towards West End, past the Fox Hotel, past the Pig. A spring breeze cools the night and my dress floats in it. We talk about Jules Verne and *Twenty Thousand Leagues Under the Sea*, we talk about *The Office* (UK, obviously), we talk about my kids. The street is quiet and I realise how late it is, but Anthony slips his hand into mine as we cross the road, and I forget again. Running my thumb across his, my stomach turns on itself.

In the weeks after I left Borhan, my brother booked a massage for me at a nearby spa hotel. When the masseuse threaded his fingers through mine to massage my hand,

I started crying. I couldn't stop. I didn't move or make a sound, salty water just poured down my cheeks and onto the table. Years of tension released by the joining of a stranger's palm with mine. Palm to palm is holy palmers' kiss.

'Your hands are soft,' I say to Anthony.

'You bet,' he says. 'That's what happens when you avoid manual labour your whole life.' I laugh. We talk about Toowoomba, we talk about debutante balls in country towns, we talk about Philip Seymour Hoffman. We buy ice-creams at the 7-Eleven on Boundary Street and take them across the road to a little inner-city garden, fairy lights strung overhead, a few people scattered about. The usual collection of West End misfits. Druggies, leftie yuppies and roaming teens. Both of us are at home in the fray, me eating a Bubble-O-Bill in mulberry fur, him with fake blood under his nails.

A kid in a hoodie scooters past, chewing on a kebab, shouting to his mate, 'It was a fuckin' possum, bro!'

'Nah man, it was a rat.'

We find an empty bench on the edge of the park and sit down together with our ice-creams. He eats his Maxibon biscuit-end first, his fingers melting into the chocolate. I point out the absurdity of his technique. He valiantly refuses to change. 'Sometimes the heart just wants what the heart wants.' We talk about Liam and Noel Gallagher's ongoing feud, we talk about the magnificent Portuguese tarts at the West End Deli, we talk about the resurgence of the mullet as an acceptable hairstyle, concurring that it isn't. We stop talking and I'm accosted with steady blue-grey.

'You look really beautiful tonight,' he says easily.

'So do you! I mean, not beautiful, but you know . . . what I meant was, is, you look nice, too.'

'You take compliments well.'

'Often it's much worse,' I grimace.

He smiles.

'Why is your little boy so far away?' I ask boldly, all of a sudden filled with the need to discuss something real. 'Is that okay to ask?'

'Of course it is,' he says, eyes trained on the grass under our feet. 'He's up there with his mum. Her family lives up north. I came up as far as Brissy to close the gap, to be closer to him. I could still work here, at least. She's such a wonderful mother, and he's smitten with her. Sydney was a hard time . . . and, her and I . . . we just never worked. And then we just couldn't land in the same place . . .' He takes a breath, clears his throat, looks me in the eye.

'I'm sorry,' I say, wondering if I should have pried. 'That can't be easy.'

'It's okay.' He's stoic now, but Mercutio underneath. I nod and fix my gaze on him without speaking, sensing there is more to say. He meets me there. 'But, I mean, it isn't. It's hard. He's the most beautiful boy . . .' he trails off. 'Anyway . . . she's the best mum she can be up there. And that matters.'

'What is he like? Your son.'

'He's an angel . . . well, mostly. But, the gentlest boy. He's funny too, a real original.' A smile takes his eyes. 'You know, you'd always hope that when you hold your kid, you want it to be the safest they'll ever feel in this world. But I realised when I held him close to me . . . it's the safest I've ever felt. His hair, his skin. He just feels like . . . home. Where I'm meant to be.'

Anthony breathes out. A cloud moves over the moon. The fairy lights above our heads brighten against the night. I feel a maternal uprising for this man I barely know, the need to boil soup, or fill a hot water bottle, to tell him how I know how to press things tight inside myself in just the same way he's doing now, and how he needs to let out everything he's holding back or it will find its own way to leak out into the world. But since we have only spent a few brief hours together, I take his hand in my own and say, inadequately, 'It's going to be okay.' He clears his throat, sealing up the cracks with consummate skill. We sit in the wake of it all for a moment.

'But on to the real debate . . .' he says, leaning into me conspiratorially, his face centimetres from mine. 'What do we think? A rat, or a fuckin' possum?'

This time, I kiss him. And it's not funny, and it's not clever. It's like laying a basket of sorrow into a river and watching it float away, until the river bends to reeds.

The evening ends with the wind blowing a plastic pie wrapper past us, the sound of two drunks fighting, and a cabbie lighting a cigarette, leaning on his bonnet, talking to the Lebanese owner of the burger joint. I order an Uber and offer Anthony a lift, but again he says he'll walk home. 'It's not far.' We wait on the kerb, our arms touching. Amritpal pulls up in his Toyota Corolla, and I turn to Anthony. 'Here it is,' I say.

'Thanks for coming to see the show,' he says, pulling me in for a quick hug.

'Yeah,' I say, kissing him quickly on the lips . . . 'I love you.'

He doesn't miss a beat, unlike my heart, which stops immediately.

'See ya,' he says kindly, as I get into the Uber.

I force my face into a smile and wave goodbye through the window as Amritpal does a U-turn and starts up the hill, far enough away for me to unfreeze, rhythmically beat the back of my head against the headrest, and release a torrent of expletives that would make Nick Kyrgios blush.

'Is everything okay?' asks Amritpal, cautiously.

'What the fuck is wrong with me?' I say to the road.

To his credit, Amritpal simply nods silently, and drives on.

The next morning I wake to the sound of my neighbours driving their kids to netball. Last night comes back to me in technicolour and a groan of embarrassment escapes my lips even before my feet touch the rug. I slip on my Ugg boots and grab my phone, scrolling through my past numbers as I flick on the kettle and wait for it to boil. Andy picks up after two rings.

'How did it go? Tell me everything.'

I explain the night with surgical precision, describing not only the glory of the evening and the delight I took in every moment of his company, but the excruciating goodbye and subsequent way I lay in bed with my face in the pillow, hoping to die a quick death.

Silence.

'Ands? Did you hear me? I said I loved him! On our second date!'

'Just processing.'

I hold the phone between my ear and shoulder to pour my tea. I chuck in some sugar, splash in the milk, and dip the bag in and out furiously, as if the movement will speed up the brewing process or change the past.

'I don't know why I said it, it just slipped out. I'm not even sure he heard it. But what if he did? Obviously, I don't love him. I've just met him! I mean I could love him, eventually. He's bloody wonderful. But it wasn't even that kind of "I love you". I said it like I was saying goodbye to one of the kids, you know? Like: kiss, hug, I love you, go to school, bye.'

'Seets, I get it. Be cool. It's all good. He won't even be thinking on it.'

I put the milk back in the fridge and shut the door with my foot, sipping my tea. It burns my top lip.

'Should I text him about it?'

'Nooooo,' she says slowly. 'What if he didn't hear it, and you text him, and it's the first he's hearing of it? That's probably not ideal. How about you just leave it?'

'Yep. You're right. I'll leave it.'

I do not leave it.

I stew about it all day. I type several lengthy texts and delete them, letter by letter. I make wild assumptions about him ranging from 'maybe he's partially deaf and didn't hear me' to 'now he thinks I'm a clinger and will never speak to me again'. In short, I overthink the situation with Olympic prowess.

Eventually, settling on tone and style (self-deprecating, genuine and brief), I text him later that afternoon:

> *Awkward, but I think as I got into the Uber last night, I may have said . . . 'I love you.'*
>
> *I don't know why I did that. Maybe just the familiarity of a kiss and cuddle goodbye?*
>
> *I sat in the Uber and decided whether or not to end my existence.*

I didn't even have a chance to pour myself a drink before he replied:

> *Hey, look, totally heard it.*
>
> *But I knew it was nothing more than an endearing slip of the tongue. We've all done that shit.*
>
> *Still. Was kinda sweet, nonetheless.*
>
> *You a funny lady x*

I put my phone down, pour myself a drink and sip it, smiling like a fool at the fair.

1946. Tehran.

Dolly wrapped her boxy, tweed coat tightly around her chest and pulled down her woollen hat. She took her snuff box out of her pocket, pulled a pinch of powder between her thumb and pointer finger, and sniffed it sharply up her nose. Feeling the wave hit her, she walked slowly home in the almost-night, with a basket of sewing over her left arm, and a bag of used rags on her right. The war. It was over, but it was not over. There had been bad harvests. The Brits and the Soviets had bled the nation's resources dry. There wasn't enough food, or work, and now she was without a husband. Her in-laws were old. There was some money, but who knew how long it was going to last. She pulled a handful of keshmesh from her pocket, chewing the dried grapes slowly as she walked home. The streets of Tehran are named for poets. Hafez, Saadi, Tabrizi, Rumi; men who write about truth and love and the soul like they have seen the face of the divine. Poetry floats in the air of Tehran like dust. As Dolly walked through the cold laneways, the words of Saadi came to her: 'The rose and the thorn and sorrow and gladness are linked together.'

Dolly cleaned houses during the day. In the evenings, she sewed. She took in dresses, shirts and trousers for alteration and repair. In the current climate, people could not afford new clothes, and were often too skinny for their old ones. She had many customers.

Dolly had just left the home of Behrooz and Shirin Mahdavi. She cleaned for them on Thursdays. The young couple were unable to bring a child into this world. Even though they had tried and tried, no baby would come to them. They were a sweet pair. Good Bahá'ís, married just before the war. Behrooz worked at the Bank Melli Iran, on Ferdowzi Avenue. Shirin helped her mother with a small catering business, decorating sweets, but only because she would otherwise be bored. They had more than enough money for her to spend her days as she saw fit. As Shirin and her mother prepared zoolbia in saffron syrup, sholezard, rose-petal gaz and pistachio halwa, they talked non-stop about the royal family. They idolised the Shah and his glamorous wife, Queen Fawzia. Shirin wanted her hair and her eyebrows to match the queen's exactly. Two rolls at the front, held with gold and pearl slide clips, and a curled bob at the back. As she watched the little Princess Shahnaz grow, Shirin prayed every night for a little girl of her very own.

Dolly could see her house at the end of the lane. She stopped and took a deep breath. The air passing out of her mouth was like smoke in the cold night. Dolly knew there were forty-eight steps between where she stood and the gate. In the time it took her to walk those forty-eight steps, she would decide which of her daughters to give to the Mahdavis. She began to walk, but in truth, she already knew which answer would come.

Mehri was too old. Mona was too wild. Khodi was a boy, and it would be foolish to give away her only son. Fari was just five years old, and her baby. Dolly swallowed a keshmesh and felt it catch in her throat as she reached the stone wall of their compound. She had made her choice. She would give Irie away.

Irie was her most beautiful daughter. Shirin Mahdavi would like that. She had light caramel skin. A tiny, perfect nose. Her cheeks blushed cherry when she laughed. She was quiet and poised. She had a prepossessing, biddable nature. And most importantly, she loved sweets. Irie would like the Mahdavis, and their beautiful home and their beautiful things, and Dolly would see her when she went to clean it. Yes, it would have to be her pretty Irie.

It wouldn't be forever, Dolly told herself. Just for a few years, while the family got back on their feet. One less mouth to feed was one less mouth to feed.

The next morning, Dolly pulled together a few things in a small bag, and helped Irie dress in her warmest things. She told her she was going to live in a beautiful palace with lovely food to eat, toys to play with, and books to read. She told her she would have sweets whenever she felt like it, and a bath every night if she wanted. Dolly didn't cry, and she didn't waste time. She knew that if the handover took any longer than a few moments, she wouldn't do it.

When they arrived at the white stone doors of the Mahdavi residence, Irie smiled and kissed her mamaan on both cheeks. Shirin Mahdavi was ready with a doll for her. A porcelain doll with black ringlets and a yellow dress with tiny, white, embroidered flowers. She held Irie's hand as they waved goodbye to Dolly.

That night, after a dinner of saffron rice, red currants and sweet chicken, Irie sat up in her own bed and looked around her own room. She fingered the pink sheets. Girl sheets.

The coverlet was rose. Irie adored roses. There was a shelf with books on it, and trinkets, and beside it on the floor was a little wooden house, filled with small pieces of delicately carved furniture, just for dolls. In this house, even the dolls had their own beds. Her family's house didn't have as much furniture as the teeny, tiny house in front of her. Today, she had played with the small furniture and the little house and she had felt happy and rich and surrounded with fine friends. The dolls were wonderful company. But the magic had left with the sun, and now Irie was alone.

Irie had never been alone at night. For seven years she had slept against the soft bodies of her sisters, listening to their breathing and their snores. Rabbits in a burrow. Now, the large pink bed seemed to her like a raft; a raft floating in the middle of a dark, wide sea, with nothing and no one to be seen for miles. As she thought about her family, she felt her mouth slowly gawp. Irie began to wail. She wailed and wept and moaned. She spared no cry. Sitting up on her knees, clutching the rose coverlet with balled fists, she keened, sobbing.

Shirin and Behrooz came running in to comfort her. They held her and wiped her face, and asked her what they could bring her to make her feel better, but Irie would not be stopped. She wept and shouted for her mother to come. She cried, 'Mamaan, Mamaan, Mamaan!' until eventually, she fell asleep, completely exhausted. Shaking, the Mahdavis went back to their bedroom.

The next day was the same. And the next. And the next. Irie cried and shouted for a full week. Fuelled by all the rich food she was being fed, she wept and wailed and threw tantrum after tantrum, only stopping to stuff a piece of halwa or gaz in her mouth before crying some more.

On the seventh day, Dolly came to clean the Mahdavis' house. Shirin Mahdavi greeted her white-faced at the door, with Irie in tow.

'Dowlat-khanum, we want a child, but we don't want a stolen one. Here, she is yours.'

Dolly pulled Irie into her coat and kissed her head and squeezed her cheeks and rubbed her back. Her eyes were red.

'Have you been crying?' Irie asked her mother. Dolly nodded and sniffed. 'Me too,' said Irie.

Together they walked home. When they got to the top of the lane, it took less than forty-eight steps for Dolly to make her next decision. She would pack up all of her children, and return to India.

In the same forty-eight steps, seven-year-old Irie also made a decision. She would grow up quickly, and once she did, she would never be poor again.

1947. Iran/Pakistan border.

'I have told you, Madam, and I am telling you again, it has not arrived.'

'And I have told you, Agha Hooshmani, I cannot wait another day.'

'Madam, these things take time.'

Jamshid Hooshmani was a patient man. They say there are patient people, and then there are people who manage visa and passport affairs at rural border crossings in the Middle East. Jamshid was both. The war had seen Zahedan transformed from a sleepy village on the border of Iran and Pakistan to a bustling provincial administrative centre. This was all well and good for the bazaar traders and kebab vendors, but this was not the life Jamshid had envisioned for himself in his quiet youth – stamping passports, arguing with weary travellers over delayed visas, expired passports, and the unhurried bureaucratic processes of the Post National Company of Iran. Actually, he had always wanted to be a pilot, but his lazy eye and the shock onset of type one diabetes after a burst appendix in his teens had put paid to his dreams of flight. Here he sat, week after week, in the Zahedan border control office – a small cement bunker at the edge of a salt desert, the Dasht-e Lut – 'emptiness plain'. His hair was neatly combed, and his brown shirt with yellow epaulettes pressed perfectly by his small wife, Zainab. His shoes were polished to a shine, his long trousers tyrannical in the July heat. His slight form made even slighter by the large desk he sat behind, welcoming a shifty hot breeze through the window of the visa office, and an even shiftier clientele through the front door.

Dolly was not a patient woman, but her husband had been a patient man, and she had learnt how to take things slowly with people whose insides didn't churn in the ways hers did. She had been coming to this office for a week now, every day, five children in tow, smiling and gentle and sweet as pie, and every day she was compassionately but firmly turned away by a man who looked like he needed a decent meal and a pair of correctional spectacles. This was because her visa had not yet arrived and he had no way of knowing when it would. She feared she had outstayed her welcome at the home of a local Bahá'í who had offered to take her and the children in while she waited to cross the border into Pakistan. Her plan was to travel overland to India, where she had a sister, seven nieces and nephews, and a bungalow waiting for her. What little patience she had left was being whittled to a sharp point by her children, who were hot, bored, hungry and sick of travelling.

'Agha Hooshmani,' Dolly said steadily, 'I am telling you that I cannot wait another day, and that is because my five children and I have nowhere to sleep tonight.'

Mehri's, Mona's, Irie's and Khodi's ears pricked up, and they turned to their mother in silence. Fari pulled at her mother's earlobe with a chubby hand, and rested her head on Dolly's bony shoulder, sucking her thumb sweetly.

'If you do not figure out a way to send us across that border today, then my children and I will have no choice but to sleep right here under this desk, or come home with you.'

With that she stood up, pulled Fari onto her hip, took Irie's hand, and headed for the door, followed nimbly by her older children.

'We will wait outside, Agha Hooshmani, until you let us know what to do.'

Jamshid scratched his sparse moustache and sniffed. Summer always brought on his allergies. He liked Dolly. She was tall and thin, with an elegant face and a soft wave in her dark hair. She spoke gently, but in a way that made you understand that her tongue could lash you if it had cause. She reminded him of his own mother. Her children kept close to her like ducklings. On the first day he had asked after her husband and she had said he was with God. She had asked about his family too, and on the second day she had brought a small honey cake for his wife. Jamshid had secretly eaten it on his way home and had felt a little bit guilty when on the third day Dolly had asked how his wife had enjoyed the cake. He had told her over-enthusiastically that Zainab had loved it and wanted the recipe. If she followed him home tonight, his lie would be exposed. Then again, Allah be praised, he could not let a lone woman with five children sleep on the floor of the border bunker! It would be a terrible sin.

So, Jamshid Hooshmani did something he had never done before. He cleared his throat, opened his top drawer, took out his stamp and stamped Dolly's passport: 'VISA APPROVED'.

Outside, in the shade of a scrub oak, Mehri turned to her mother and said, 'But Shaheen-Khanum didn't throw us out, Mamaan. Why did you say we had nowhere to sleep?'

'Will we really go home with that man, Mamaan?' asked Irie, her little brow furrowed.

'No, baby, no,' said Dolly, pulling a slab of flatbread out of her handbag and tearing it into six strips. She put her own piece into her mouth as she sat cross-legged on the dusty ground.

Mona stared at Irie taking small bites of her bread, little nibbles like a mouse. Her bread was already finished. 'Then why did you say we would sleep here? Why did you lie to him?'

The breeze had lifted and was blowing the dust under the scrub oak into little eddies around the base of the tree, picking up dry leaves.

'Jaanam, there are two types of lies – ones that God hears, and ones He doesn't. If you tell a lie big enough for God to hear, you will choke on it.'

'How do you know which lies God can hear?'

'Ah, well,' she said with a smile, 'to know that you have to know God.'

'Do you know God?' Mona asked, her deep brown eyes wide.

It was a good question, and one that Dolly had considered every day since she lost Behmaan.

'I know enough to know that the lie I told that man won't stick in my throat,' she said, as she pushed the last bite of her bread into Mona's open mouth.

1985. Toowoomba.

'Fari, Sita-koo?'

'Maman, she's fine,' Fari said impatiently, hurrying through the linoleum-floored kitchen and into the bathroom to blow-dry her wet hair. Rahnee was perfecting the art of eighties fringe sculpting in the mirror. She had recently read a *Dolly* magazine article called 'Tress to Impress' and was fuzzing and teasing her fringe to a kind of high and messy sideways flick – just like Madonna.

'Fine, yes, but koo? Where?' asked Dolly, laying a rolled chapati into a hot pan and pushing it down with a tea towel.

'Go find your sister,' said Fari to Rahnee, switching on the hairdryer and pulling a round brush roughly through her long bob. She was running late for work.

'She's fine, Grans,' said Rahnee, coming into the kitchen. She kissed Dolly on the cheek and picked up a steaming chapati from the pile, dunking the jammy knife into the butter and then back into the cherry jam, spreading it thickly.

'She's fine. She's fine. Where is she fine?' muttered Dolly, deftly flipping the flatbread. 'Nobody is watching this baby.'

'She's not a baby! She's four!' laughed Rahnee, admiring her reflection in the oven glass, her mouth full and dripping with jam.

Jamal dribbled a soccer ball down the hallway and into the kitchen. 'Grans, have you seen my shin pads?'

'Come and eat.'

'Yeah but have you seen them? I need them today.'

'Come. Eat. I'll get it. Sita-koo?'

'I just saw her. She was crossing the road by herself,' said Jamal.

Dolly smiled and squeezed his cheek, putting a large plate of hot chapatis into his hand and wiping her floury hands on her apron.

'I can't eat all of this, Grans. I'll have one,' he said, handing back the plate and quickly stuffing a dry chapati into his mouth.

'Only one! No. One chapati and you won't be able to run and play this ball game you like. Have more,' Dolly said, pushing another one into his hands.

'It's called soccer, Grans.' He took the chapati, but gingerly flicked it back on top of the pile when her back was turned.

'Yes, "soccer" . . . all the mans running after one small ball. Why not give them all a ball?' she asked. Rahnee giggled.

Turning off the stove, Dolly buttered a fresh chapati, spread some jam on, rolled it tightly and put it in her apron pocket. Then she went to rifle through some baskets on the landing of the back stairs, pulling out shin pads and some soccer boots and pushing them into Jamal's bag.

'Sita!' she called to the backyard from the top of the stairs, her thick, lilting voice taking to the wind like an arrow. 'Where are you, Baba? Breakfast!'

'Mama Doll! Must the whole neighbourhood hear you shouting?' exclaimed John, flushing the downstairs loo and emerging from its cobwebbed depths, newspaper in hand.

'John, go eat chapati and I'll come make you coffee,' Dolly said, shuffling down the stairs and past him, continuing to holler.

He could never understand the absurd need his mother-in-law had to have her eye on his youngest child at all times, under all circumstances. The fact was, Dolly asked 'Sita-koo?' so often, people had begun using it as her name. Then again, the raising of small children was not in John's purview. He saw himself coming into his own as a parent once the children had gained a somewhat meaningful grasp of basic philosophy, science, mathematics and language; when they were able to hold an elegant conversation, and a knife and fork. Spoon feeding and sandpits were not for John Walker. Sita was a bonnie little thing, though. His precious treasure. She liked to crawl up him occasionally and sit on his lap or shoulders, or put her skinny little arms around his neck and kiss his closely shaved cheeks. It had not escaped John's notice that she was fairly wild – always whizzing around barefoot in the yard or hiding under the furniture in the house – or that she still drank milk from a baby bottle even though she was nearly five. He probably would have said something about this if she was his first child, but being his fourth she was granted special liberties, certain ways of going unnoticed and unchecked, unpruned. Hopefully like a sweet pea vine, and not twelve acres of lantana. God knows where she was, but John wasn't concerned about it. She always turned up. Dolly always found her.

Rahnee and Jamal thumped down the back stairs, schoolbags slung over their shoulders.

'Ma! We're going!' Rahnee called, straddling her Redline bike.

'Lunch! Lunch!' called Dolly frantically from the yard.

Jamal ran back up the stairs and came back with two paper bags, throwing one at Rahnee and stuffing the other in his bag. 'Bye, Grans!' he shouted.

There was a lot of shouting at Bridge Street. John had tried valiantly to encourage his family to adopt a more genteel way of communicating, but Dolly didn't like quiet children, she liked commotion. If a child was shouting and making noise, you knew they weren't starving, they weren't sick and they weren't lost. She waved to Jamal and Rahnee and saw Fari rushing down the back stairs to her car, keys in hand.

'Maman, man raftam!' Fari called on the fly. Mum, I'm off.

'Sita-koo?!'

'She's okay!' said Fari, shaking her brown lunch bag in the air before Dolly could ask her about it, revving her Toyota Corona, and reversing too quickly down the dirt driveway.

'Yavosh boro! Ya-Khodah!' Dolly bellowed. Slow down! My God!

Dolly walked the length of the yard, past the garages and the jacaranda tree not yet in bloom, calling for her grand-daughter, her house slippers becoming wet in the dewy grass.

Behind the tennis shed, a worn timber hut with several palings missing and a corrugated tin roof that was rusted from years of neglect, Sita was crouched barefoot among a pile of terracotta pots, wearing a pink nightie with little red hearts on it. She was lifting each pot gingerly and inspecting the dirt underneath, pushing it around with small soil-covered fingers – the same fingers she now used to push her dark hair, some of which was still held hostage in yesterday's ponytail, off her face, leaving muddy streaks on her cheeks and nose.

She was searching for slaters. Little armadillo-like beetles that rolled into balls when you poked them or disrupted their daily routine of burrowing, sleeping and crawling into dark crevices. They lived under pots or in piles of timber, and where there was one, there was usually a horde. Sita was collecting them in a plastic takeaway container half filled with dirt, because she loved them. She loved poking them with the tip of her finger and watching them roll up into a tight little ball, picking them up gently and putting them on her flat palm, seeing how long it would take for them to tentatively unroll, stretch out their tiny legs and shuffle about in her hand, trying to work out how to get back to their family in the dirt. She would wait until they were bravely crawling about before lowering her small palm into the container, and letting them find their way down to the habitat she had created for them.

Dolly rounded the tennis shed and saw her granddaughter crouched in the grass. She was relieved. At balance again.

'My sunshine, where have you been? What are you doing?'

'Grandma, look!' Sita said, holding up her new pets.

'Ah ha. A family, is it?' replied Dolly, lowering herself down slowly to sit on a large overturned pot.

'Yes, a family.'

'Come, show me. Come tell me, what are their names?' Dolly reached down, wiped Sita's dirty face with the hem of her loose house dress, took the chapati roll out of her pocket and held it to the little girl's mouth. Sita took a large bite, leant in to her grandmother and introduced her to each slater, making up names for them, talking as she chewed. Bert, Ernie, Mary, Benita, John. When Sita had finished the chapati, Dolly wiped her mouth again and stood up with a creak. Her knees were swollen and arthritic, but her back was still strong. She started picking up pieces of broken terracotta, tidying up the sharp shards of a pot that was probably hit with a cricket ball, singing 'You Are My Sunshine' as she worked.

'Again,' muttered Sita, still excavating beneath the pots. 'Sing sunshine again.' Dolly sang it again, both verses, and Sita joined in without taking her eyes off the slaters in the dirt.

Dolly thought of India. The sound of it, the smell of sandalwood and cumin and raw sewage and dried mint, and tea. There was a garden out the back of the bungalow with pots like this, growing bits and pieces – chilli, bay leaf, coriander going to seed. Neymat and Khodi used to play cricket behind the house. She heard the crack of the ball against the pots and her own voice scolding them as she cut green beans into a bucket near her bare feet.

Upstairs, John made his own coffee, ate several excellent chapatis, and headed off to work.

1943. Tehran.

Mona stared through the dusty glass of the local nân-waieh. Behind her, a line of dusty, tired people clutching coupons stretched down the street, and in it, her sister Mehri, holding the hand of her little brother, Khodi. Mona's stomach was too empty to gurgle, and she felt light-headed, but she never missed a trip to the bakery. Her favourite bread to stare at was the sangak.

Taking the patience and skill of two bakers, Persian nân-e sangak is, quite simply, the Rolls-Royce of breads. First, the dough is mixed, rolled and stretched by four hands into an elongated, flat slab. Then it is thrust into an oven and rested on a bed of hot pebbles for a few minutes before being removed by a long, double-pronged fork, and slid onto a stone bench, hot and flat, fluffy, slightly flaky, a touch crispy, and sort of doughy. A fresh and steamy feast, ready to be torn into pieces and shoved into the lucky gob of some pocket-jangling Esfandiar.

Monavahr's pockets were empty. There was no money to buy nân-e sangak, let alone the even more mouth-watering, sesame topped sangak. She didn't even have anything to barter with the local kids for a few rials. Mehri had the coupon and would be given one medium-sized cob. She would ask for more. She would tell the vendor that her mother had five children to feed and that her father was very sick in the bemorestan. But she would come away with one cob like everyone else, and she wouldn't fight. Even though she was only twelve, Mehri maintained her dignity like a dove. She never threw herself at the bars of the cage. Mona would fight. But Mona wasn't in charge.

It's okay, Mona thought. Ammu Kekku is coming tonight.

Their father's much younger brother, Kekku, was Mona's favourite, and she was his. Kekku loved Mona's fearlessness, her inability to look ahead. Something about her hyper-focus on the here-and-now appealed to Kekku just as much as it frustrated everybody else. It made him think, as he rolled his tobacco into thin paper and licked it, that perhaps life wasn't so bad. Perhaps the kid was on to something. If you only had to worry about what was happening right now, you could be happy. Kekku knew Mona had potential. He didn't know in what way, but he knew she would make something of herself in this world, and she wouldn't take anybody's shit.

Mona had two gears: happy and angry. She was never put in charge of anything, because she would do such a rough job of it that it would need to be redone by someone with more patience. But she was great fun, and almost pathologically brave. A stray dog once bit her on the ankle, and instead of running away, she grabbed it and bit it back – on the nose. Kekku chuckled to himself remembering the dog yelping. Dolly said she was wild and there was nothing to be done but to send her out with the boys, so Khodi became her constant companion, and they grew wrapped up in each other like tree roots.

Kekku arrived that evening to find Mona and Khodi excavating the front compound of the Prophet's house. It was filled with old stones, broken furniture, bits of timber. The Bahá'ís didn't want to draw attention to the fact that this house was holy to them, or special in any way. Maintaining it with the reverence they knew it deserved would only make the Islamic authorities suspicious, and then they would lose the property to the teeth of the Mulla's bulldozers. Mona and Khodi had dug a large hole and found a sandstone tile underneath the layers of dust and dirt. Together, they were digging and scraping and sweeping – revealing a beautifully tiled courtyard underneath the rubbish.

'Monavahr! Jaanam! Where are you digging to? America?' Kekku called out the back door.

'Kekku!' she screeched, happiness at full throttle, running filthy and ragged into his arms, with Khodi following like a darting squirrel.

'I brought you a present. Not that you deserve it, you daughter of a mongoose,' Kekku said with a glint.

Mona was so excited she put her arms around him and pressed her fingernails hard into his back. Kekku yelped and laughed and jumped out of her grasp.

'What is it?!' she yelled, advancing on him again.

'Don't bite me, wildcat! Stay back!' he laughed, assuming the pose of a crouching samurai, ready to defend his person.

'What is it?!' both children shrieked again, busting out of their sandals.

'Okay, okay!' he said, putting his arms up. 'It's skates. Skates!'

Kekku worked at the skating rink in the middle of the capital, and he had procured an old pair of rink skates for very little money. The skates had been on the feet of thousands and the inner soles were brown from it. The laces were grey and frayed. The wheels were well-worn and scuffed. But Mona didn't care. She saw only potential.

Demanding them immediately from Kekku, Mona took her new skates to the dirt alleyway behind the house, and put them on over knitted socks. She practised skating up and down the dirt road, underneath rows of flapping washing, while Khodi watched. For a week, she threw herself into learning to skate, which is always faster if you don't mind bleeding.

Mona's attitude to risk had always been to take in abundance, and she saw these skates for what they were – collateral. Putting her knees and elbows on the line was merely the price she had to pay for what she hoped would be a hefty return, but it was very important that she made skating look as easy as walking. When the word spread about her skates, every bachah in the neighbourhood would want a turn, and she planned to show them how easy it was. She planned to make the pock-holed street look as smooth and easy to skate on as the Azadi velodrome.

Being so singular minded, it didn't take long for her to become proficient, so when she took her rickety skates to the street, zipping up and down the road like it was the simplest thing in the world, business boomed. There were so many takers clamouring for a turn, she even hired out the skates separately. Three rials for one skate. Five rials for two. Pigeon-toed Reza Sinai begged to pay with a sweet biscuit, which she allowed on the fault of her stomach, but everyone else paid cash. Nobody was brave enough to bargain with her.

When night fell, and the kites left the purple sky, and the rich bachehas of Tehran went home to their fat dinners of chicken, rice and sour-currants, Mona took her skates and her heavy pockets home to her own mamaan. She called to her sisters, Khodi, and baby Fari, and emptied her cash out onto the thin rug with a confident clatter. Dolly, wiping her hands on her apron, gasped at the sight of the money, preparing to drag Mona by her ears back to whoever she had robbed, a forgiveness prayer already touching her lips – but Mona quickly explained her savvy dealings, and left no small detail out.

Mehri smiled, Khodi laughed and jumped about. Dolly kissed both her red cheeks and said, 'Che zerang, che che zerang! Bah bah, jaanam. Bah bah!' How clever. So, so clever, well done my darling, well done.

'Tomorrow,' replied Mona with a grin. 'Tomorrow we eat nân.'

1993. Toowoomba.

Dolly took a brown egg from the cardboard carton and held it in her warm hands. She whispered a prayer over it and passed it over her granddaughter's head in slow anticlockwise circles, like stirring a pot of thick soup. She rolled the egg softly over Sita's skinny, tanned arms and slender back, as she sat with her nose in a Nancy Drew novel, crunching a carrot. Dolly was drawing the curse of the evil eye out of her granddaughter's body and up into the egg's thin, crisp shell. This ancient art of oomancy, Dolly believed, drew wickedness out of the bones. The wickedness, this bad energy, was caused by someone giving the bearer the evil eye, a curse of envy, of being watched and wished ill upon. Her granddaughter was very beautiful and very clever. There was always a chance somebody would be jealous of her, and cast upon her the evil eye.

Satisfied with her work, she closed her hand over the defiled egg, shuffled to the back landing and looked out onto the orange brick pavers that formed a small courtyard at the bottom of the steps. John was pegging towels onto the clothesline, humming Verdi's *La Traviata*. He hung the mismatched linen by the short edge, sharing one peg between two towels. Even, neat, efficient, like a row of teeth. Dolly watched him for a minute and thought what she always thought: John was a very good man who paid an extraordinary amount of attention to a few things, and none at all to other more important things. She muttered a prayer over the egg, and lobbed it enthusiastically off the back stoop. It cracked on the pavers, splattering yolk and white and shell in all directions – a yellowy firework of vanquished wickedness.

John, jumping at the sound, turned to see the eggy pavers. His ears flushed with blood. 'You know, this is utter superstition!' he chastised Dolly, abandoning the washing and unrolling the neatly coiled garden hose from the tap behind the outdoor loo. He twisted the nozzle to 'stream' and maximised the pressure, aggressively hosing the eggshells, yolk and curses off the pavers and onto the grass before they dried on the bricks. 'Don't do that again!' he said. 'Waste of eggs! Messes up the pavers! It's completely ridiculous!'

'What is "superstition"?' Dolly replied, nonplussed on the stoop.

'Superstition means you have an irrational belief in the super-natural. This sort of nonsense!' He gestured to the egg with flappy hands. 'The belief that someone can put evil spirits into you by looking at you a certain way, that dreams mean some-thing, that you can read the future in a cup of tea! It's rubbish!'

Dolly thought for a minute. '"Supernatural" means what?'

'Something beyond the laws of science and nature – some-thing we can't understand – like angels and demons and evil spirits.'

'Ah ha. Angels and demons! I know. In Farsi we say "fereshteh" and "shaytoon" . . .'

'Yes, like that.'

Dolly thought for a moment as John turned off the hose. 'Like God, too, I think,' she said mildly.

'Well, God is different,' said John, preparing to launch into a series of well-versed theological proofs concerning the nature of God, the knowledge of God through his Prophets or Manifestations and the existence of one omnipotent God, rather than many lesser gods. But Dolly had left the stoop and was already in the kitchen, peeling a tray of half-bruised mangoes.

She peeled them with a short paring knife, whole, like a potato. She cut off the unbruised chunks and diced them into a container, slipping a couple into her mouth along the way. She thought of her youngest sister, Siloo, and how the dead can be conjured up in a second, against your will, by a whiff of perfume, the sound of a nut cracking, the feel of a woollen sleeve on skin. Siloo loved mangoes.

There was a lot that people didn't understand about what existed and what didn't. A loaf of bread does not exist unless it is in your hands. Unless you can hold it, tear it, and put pieces of it into your mouth, it has no effect. Unless it can take away your hunger or the hunger of your children, a loaf of bread is nothing. But words are different. Words have power, even when you cannot hear them. If you believe words whispered alone in prayer can take effect, can sail from your lips to God's ear, leaving life's troubles in their wake, then you cannot disbelieve that an envious look can have just as much effect. Men always pretended to understand everything. They were obsessed with finding proof – desperate to say that some things were true and some things were false. Desperate to tell everybody why they were right and the last man was wrong. Dolly had lived long enough to understand that you could never truly understand anything – least of all truth.

What were messed pavers to ridding her granddaughter of the evil eye? What was it to hose the juice of an egg off bricks when you had mopped the fevered brow of a dying husband, wiped poison from the lips of a dead sister, seen the lifeless body of your son wash up on the shore of a foreign beach, and watched your granddaughter's coffin lowered into the ground before her eighteenth birthday?

Dolly slipped another piece of mango into her mouth, and wiped her cheek with the back of her wrist.

John rolled the hose away neatly and went back to hanging the washing.

2017. Brisbane.

I have strep-throat. I've been living in the new house, The Shack, for a month, been single for a month, and now I can't swallow. I'm shivering. Sweating. Sniffing. Hocking. Borhan has taken the kids so that I can recover. We've only been living like this for a few weeks, so they aren't used to going back and forth yet. I would worry about them, but I'm too sick to care.

My phone rings. It's Aunty Mehri. She doesn't waste time with pleasantries.

'Take Panadol, Sita!'

'Hi Aunty . . .'

'You want me to come to you? I can come.'

'I don't want you to get sick, Aunty,' I rasp.

'I never get sick. Did you take Panadol? No. You didn't. That's it. I'm coming.' She lowers the phone and hollers to her son, Rumi. 'Rumi! Take me to Sita's!'

Thirty minutes later she's shuffling through the back door, a leather handbag under her arm, a red and grey woollen shawl wrapped around her shoulders. She's clutching a heavy green shopping bag. It's raining outside and her Maseur sandals are wet. I can hear them squeaking. I struggle to sit up.

'I'm here!' she calls. 'Stay there. Don't get up, Sita-koo.'

My eldest aunt puts her belongings on the dining table and starts bustling about the kitchen. I hear her fill up the kettle and flick it on, pull out a chopping board, open and close some cupboards, rattle about in the drawers. The tap runs. A pot is put on the stove. I hear the click of the gas starter and the breathy whoosh of fire as it takes.

Mehri comes into my room and sits down on the edge of my bed. Her shawl is replaced by a blue tea towel. It's flung over her left shoulder, the end damp and crumpled.

'Sita-koo, sit up and take this.'

I drag myself up and lean my back against the wall. Mehri hands me a glass of water. Her hand and the outside of the glass are both damp. She reaches into the pocket of her long cardigan and pulls out a silver packet, popping two Panadol out of it and putting them into my hand.

'I give you Nurofen as well,' she says, reaching into her other pocket. I am powerless to resist. I swallow the four pills and lie back down. They feel like tiny knives passing through my throat and gullet. Mehri picks up some clothes from my floor and my bed, cracks a window open slightly. She feels my forehead with her cool, damp hand and tut-tuts. The smell of rain mingled with exhaust fumes from the busy road and a hint of eucalyptus stirs me slightly. She's gone. I doze. She's back, a spoonful of some creamed honey in her trembling hand.

'Open your mouth,' Mehri says, putting the spoon in. The honey is slightly bitter. I haven't eaten in a couple of days because swallowing feels like razors, but it slips down more easily than I thought it would. Still, I wince.

'Okay now, sleep. I wake you up when it's ready.'

I drift off to the sound of chopping, the smell of onion and garlic. When I open my eyes, I'm drenched in sweat. My pillow is wet with it. My thighs feel stuck together, my socks damp. The smell of broth fills the moist air. I fling the doona off and roll onto my back. I test swallowing. It doesn't make me feel faint.

Mehri's soup is delicious: spicy, hot, chicken falling off the bone, herbs, plenty of onion and garlic and roughly chopped shallots. She serves it to me in bed – puts a tea towel on my lap and a deep bowl on top, half filled with soup. On the bedside table she puts a plate of buttered toast, cut into soldiers. She wipes some sweaty, matted hair off my forehead and tucks it behind my ears. Then she sits to eat with me, holding her own soup in a mug, with both hands. Mehri is about half my height, with a tidy, dark grey bob and neatly clipped fingernails. Her olive skin hangs in soft wrinkles, framing her kind eyes and knowing smile. She sits on the end of my bed and tucks one leg underneath her, an impressively limber manoeuvre for a woman in her eighties.

'Sita-koo. Tell me something. You want to tell Aunty Mehri what happened?'

She's talking about Borhan. The divorce. I love how she slips into third person, because it makes me feel like I'm about eight years old. I sip my soup and shrug my shoulders, acting eight years old. What was there to say that my mother hadn't already told her?

'Did he hit you?' she asks quietly, looking at her soup.

'Oh my god, Aunty, no,' I say quickly, my voice a husk of its former self. 'Of course not. No! Why would you think that?'

She shrugs as if to say, it happens. I suppose it does. It happens all the time.

'Do you pray, Sita?' she asks, like an eagle with its eye on a mouse.

Somehow this question hits me even harder. It hits me unexpectedly hard, and I feel myself welling up with shame. I feel like she's come here just to ask me this. I look down at my soup, clear my throat and grab a toast soldier, trying to shake off the feeling of being found out.

I grew up with prayer. I was taught to pray every morning and every night. The first words that you speak in the morning should be mention of God. The last thought you have at night should be remembrance of God. There was a time when I couldn't sleep unless I said my prayers. Like brushing my teeth. Sometimes I would wake up in the middle of the night and realise I had forgotten, sit up (because you cannot pray lying down) murmur a short verse and flop back down to sleep.

I prayed as a matter of daily servitude to God, but also for other reasons – for guidance, for assistance, for the souls of those passed – my sister's, and when I was older, my grandmother's, and the grandfathers' I never met. I was taught that praying for the souls of the departed was a way those souls would have the volition to progress spiritually, a way they could grow closer to the Almighty. The way my sister could become a spiritual giant was through my remembrance – the remembrance of a little girl in her little room, sitting up straight with her hands clasped. That, and the grace of God.

I never prayed my own prayers, only the prayers of the Prophets. I prayed the prayer for the departed so many times I could recite it easily, without the book. It began: 'Oh my God, O Thou forgiver of sins, bestower of gifts, dispeller of afflictions. Verily, I beseech thee to forgive the sins of such who have abandoned the physical garment and ascended to the spiritual world . . .' It never occurred to me that a teenage girl may not have sinned so much. I was comforted by the idea that there was some way I could help.

When my son's puppy died he wept for days. I didn't know what to do so I held him and said that prayer. I prayed for the puppy the same way I prayed for my sister and my grandmother.

Instead of being soothed, he shouted at me angrily: 'That prayer is dumb! Dusty never sinned. She was a puppy! How could she sin, Mum? There's nothing to forgive!' I wouldn't have dared question the Almighty at his age.

'I know, baby,' I said, 'but I don't know any prayers for animals.'

Before my evening prayer, I always took stock of the day that had passed:

'Bring thyself to account each day ere thou art summoned to a reckoning; for death, unheralded, shall come upon thee and thou shalt be called to give account for thy deeds.'

I wondered what it would be like to be 'summoned to a reckoning'. Had Rahnee been 'summoned'? Did she have to give an account of her deeds? Good deeds, too, or just bad deeds? A 'reckoning' doesn't exactly have positive connotations. You don't get summoned to a reckoning to talk about how well you did on that week's spelling test, or how forgiving you were when Scott Stevens said he saw your knickers on the monkey bars and called you a donkey. A reckoning is a scary prospect. So, each night I dutifully brought myself to account and prayed for forgiveness. Mostly my issue was gossip – backbiting was a grievous sin. I loved a good yarn. If God was up there with a clipboard taking notes, he definitely knew that Jessica Culthorp had told me that Frances Keenan's sister was pregnant and it was because she was a slut and Mrs Culthorp had told Jessica that she wasn't to play with Frances anymore and I had told Jessica that we just wouldn't tell her mother who we were playing with and then we had discussed who the father might be and whether or not to tell Frances what that hypocritical bitch Mrs Culthorp had said.

But as the years went by, I brought myself to account less and less. When I had small children I was too exhausted, and once I began quietly removing God from my life, or at least God's laws, not only did I not scroll through the day's good and bad deeds, I hardly prayed at all. I remember the first night of prayerless sleep. I lay my head down on the pillow, completely exhausted, and thought: God, forgive me, but I'm tired. When I woke up in the morning, the world hadn't changed, but I had. It was an emancipation. A bold revolution. The best part about it was, nobody knew. Nobody had to know. Every time I lay my head down on the pillow without praising the Lord, I felt free.

But the truth was, it was too late. Prayer was already in my bones. Like all childhood things – milk, storybooks, cuddles, kisses – prayer was a root for me. Occasionally, when I was laid low, I would pick up a book of prayer and say the verses I knew best. After my time away, the Bahá'í prayers sounded so intense to me, so full of pathos and ceremony. I felt jealous of Christians who got to make up their own prayers, use their own words to plead with God for forgiveness, or praise God for the good. They got to say exactly what they meant. If I could say what I meant, I'd start with: 'God – I know we are distant, but I spent so many years being good, when I could have been living an unexamined life. How about you take me off the roster for a while? Bench me, Lord. I don't wanna play anymore.'

I didn't think anyone would know that I secretly hung up the phone on the Almighty, but my aunts have a way of knowing things. And they love to ask.

I look at Mehri and lie to soften the blow: 'I pray sometimes, but I'm not sure God can hear me now, Aunty.'

She surprises me by laughing. A wonderful cackle that rises and overflows like a pot of boiling sugar. 'Sita-koo,' she says, smiling and putting her mug-warmed hand on my knee, 'you think God is someone to sit on his divan and listen to your prayers? God isn't having ears to hear and a mouth to speak. God doesn't need your prayers, and He isn't waiting for them.'

'So why should I pray, then?' I say, my mouth full of soup. 'Why should I bother?'

'You don't pray so that God can hear you,' she says slowly, tapping my knee with one finger. 'You pray so that you can hear God.'

1989. Toowoomba.

When a person dies too young there is a fever that takes hold. Some people let the grief burn through them all at once, taking the heat into their blood and bones and almost dying themselves. Others feel cool to the touch at first; they nurture the mourners, feed the children, clear bunches of flowers from the doorstep, only to start vomiting and blazing weeks or months later. Some people don't get sick at all.

I don't even remember feeling sad for my sister. I was only eight when she died. The stadium concert ended. The teens piled into the car. The car rolled. She was on life support. John and Fari made the choice to have it turned off. I missed a day of school.

John was a man of decisive action. When his daughter was killed, he took to the trauma like it was an explosion in a car-part factory, not even waiting for the dust to settle before he began sweeping and hosing, picking up pieces of shrapnel from the floors and walls, reassembling the shelves, reassuring the staff, reordering stock. He spoke to the doctors and the police. He organised the burial plot, the program, the music, the readings, the prayers. He notified the paper, the school, our teachers and friends, and finally, two weeks after the funeral, seeing the state of his wife, John booked a trip for two to Singapore, thinking some time away would be healing for her. Before they left, John called Mehri and asked her to come and stay at Bridge Street. Help Dolly. Walk Sita to school. Check the mail. Throw out the wilted flowers and refresh the vases and buckets with bouquets dropped on the front steps by strangers.

Mehri arrived at noon on Friday, and walked from the bus stop to Bridge Street, only to find it empty. Sita was at school, and Dolly had taken Fari for a walk to town. Just a walk. A moment to put her feet on the ground and move her legs. Nobody ever went through the front door at Bridge Street, so Mehri walked around the back. She saw the line hung with clothes. Neat, like teeth. The grass was freshly mowed as well. She could smell camphor and jasmine and pine. The yard looked ordered; no stumps or bails lying around, no stray soccer balls or cricket bats. The hose was evenly rolled and pavers free of weeds. A little spade and fork were leaning against the back steps.

The back door was open, so Mehri walked into the quiet house and kicked off her sandals. The kitchen was clean apart from half a loaf of white bread and a tub of strawberry jam sitting on the breadboard, and a few empty tea mugs in the sink. The floor was swept. The kettle was full.

When Mehri lived in Ceylon, she had a skinny house boy called Gayan. He was about sixteen, and his job was to take care of little jobs around the house – sweeping, pruning, tidying – but mostly he was there to entertain her three little sons. Gayan was excellent with the boys, playing games and roughhousing them in a gentle way, but he was fairly inept when it came to house chores. He put in little effort and was often seen leaning on a broom, daydreaming. A few months into his time with them, Gayan's mother died giving birth to his youngest sister. He stayed away for a week, and Mehri and her in-laws sent food to his family. When he came back, eyes still bloodshot, he suddenly knew how to sweep. He could clear a room of dust fastidiously, easing his grief with a laser focus on dust particles and dishes.

As Mehri opened the door to the hallway to take her little suitcase into Lisa's old room, now Sita's, where she would sleep, she heard a strange sound coming from the other end of the house. At first, she thought it might be a small animal in the front yard, possibly wounded. It sounded like a hard whimper, but was too fulsome and deep to be a child's cry. Mehri quietly put her bag down and stood still to listen. The sound grew louder and more pressed. She now knew for sure that it was human, or on the edge of human, in that space where humans and animals meet. It was a cross between a wail and a cry. Primal, like a woman deep in the throes of a contraction, or a deer hit with a hunter's arrow. It was louder now, and coming over and over again – a deep, guttural and fractured wailing.

Seeing the door to the master bedroom closed, Mehri suddenly knew who it was.

She walked nimbly back down the hallway and into the kitchen, closing the door behind her without a sound. She could still hear the cries but they were dulled by the wood and glass. Mehri took a small pot out of the kitchen cupboard and filled it to halfway with water. She threw open cupboard doors and rummaged through cluttered shelves for what she needed. Pushing the bread aside, she crushed a sprinkling of cloves, cardamom pods and black peppercorns onto the breadboard with the flat side of a knife's blade, throwing them into the water with a generous handful of black tea leaves. She found a knob of fresh ginger wrapped in foil in the door of the fridge, and threw a roughly cut slice of that in too. Turning the stove on, Mehri went outside and snapped some fresh mint from Dolly's herb garden. When the brew reached the boil, she took it off the stove, tossed in the mint, and poured in fresh milk until it was the right shade of creamy caramel, like a Werther's Original. Adding several teaspoons of brown sugar, she brought it to the boil again before pulling it off the stove and pouring it from a height, through a fine strainer, into two glasses.

Grief sits in the bones. It burrows deep into marrow and becomes a part of the way a person moves, how their eyes see the light. My aunts say that the only way to forget your sorrow is to set yourself ablaze with sacrifice. Die to yourself, your desires, your dreams, your craving for the way things were and the way things could be. Watch it all burn to the ground so that when grief comes for you all he will find is cinders, and keep walking.

Mehri opened the hallway door an inch and listened. The noise had subsided. The house was breathing with her, trying to bring the outside breezes in and draw the sadness out. Bridge Street was like that. Open windows, sunlight streaming. The timber walls were soaked with calling voices, footsteps and laughter and the clatter of pots and pans.

Mehri picked up a steaming glass of masala chai and made her way down the hall. She knocked on the door of the bedroom, and heard movement – a quick shuffling and a heavy footfall. John emerged, hair askew, his face stung and swollen as though he had fought a demon with no armour or weapons, just the clothes on his back and the teeth in his mouth.

'Drink this, John,' Mehri said gently, and held out the chai.

He reached out soundlessly and took it from her, and for a moment their eyes met. 'Sit down,' she said firmly. 'Drink it slowly.'

John cleared his throat. He meant to say 'thank you' but nothing came out.

'Sit down,' Mehri said again, nodding towards the bed.

John made his way to the edge of the bed. Mehri followed, reaching up to his shoulder and gently pressing down. He sat down slowly on the bed, the spinning world becoming still as he put the glass to his lips. The hot, milky, spiced liquid fell down his throat and it felt like a cool hand on a slapped cheek. John took a slow breath in and out.

Mehri squeezed his shoulder kindly, padded to the door and pulled it shut. She left him to his tea, and his grief.

My sister is buried under green grass and sheltering mountain trees. The high school renamed a picnic area for her and Ashley, and dedicated an annual trophy to her memory, for 'Service and Citizenship'. John and Fari present it to a new winner every speech night.

Rahnee comes back to me in moments, but I don't know if the moments are real or little films of photographs I've seen. I don't remember the way she ate, or the way she danced. I don't remember her voice. Fari says that not a day has passed in thirty-three years when she hasn't thought about her.

On her birthday in winter, my parents visit her grave to say prayers together in the wind. The inscription reads:

RAHNEE WALKER

1972–1989

BELOVED DAUGHTER OF JOHN AND FARI.

'THOU ART MY LIGHT AND MY LIGHT SHALL NEVER
BE EXTINGUISHED.'
BAHA'U'LLAH

2019. Brisbane.

It's 4pm and I'm pushing a supermarket trolley through the aisles, maintaining a deliberate pace. The kids are scattered, looking for cookie dough and ice-cream. I grab pasta. Chicken. Tomato paste. Seaweed snacks. Beef stock. Cheese slices. Leo needs a new toothbrush. Layla needs deodorant – she doesn't like the coconut one. A woman passes me with a baby in the seat of her trolley, chewing on a rusk. She's talking to it like it can understand. I used to do that with the kids. Chutney. Borhan wants to buy a puppy. His own puppy. We already have a joint custody dog called Rocky. He goes back and forth. Kelpies are a lot of work. I know that if Borhan gets a puppy of his own that somehow that puppy will also be a part of my life. The kids will love it. Rocky and the new pup will become best friends, and Borhan will be Borhan, which means that even though he may have the best of intentions, his life will get in the way, and I will end up babysitting two hounds. I emailed him about it. I literally told a grown man that he wasn't allowed a puppy. He took it poorly. Iceberg lettuce (the kids don't like the butterleaf). Bacon. Why are there so many different types of bacon? Mince – not the regular, but not the extra lean – the middle one. Bin bags. Paper towels. Frozen peas. Greek yoghurt. John and Fari both have cancer. Well, possible cancer. John is having a kidney out this week. There's a growth in it. It may be benign. Fari has a grey spot on her lung. They don't know what it is, but they can't say it's not cancer. I had to pry the information out of her. Mum doesn't believe in illness.

If I have a cold she'll tell me it's all in my mind. One day she will drop dead and her last words will be 'I'm fine'. I need to hurry. I have two classes of drafts to mark before Monday. There's a music night at the high school tomorrow, and Layla is playing the drums. They're loud. I'll need to get there early to find a park. I think about Borhan. He said my email was 'cold' and 'harsh'. I didn't think so. I thought it was reasonable. I was vulnerable. I told him I couldn't take more stress, that I was trying to remove responsibilities from my life, not add to them. That I wasn't handling things well. Now I regret saying those things. I'm ashamed. Embarrassed. Snack pack chips. A block of mint chocolate. Orange juice. Milk. Eggs. I should buy free-range, but my conscience isn't pinched enough to be concerned about barns versus open fields. I've heard the barns are overfull, but I can't be sure. I have questions around meat too. In class today, I watched a female Saudi Arabian film director talking about her work. She had to direct the outdoor scenes of her feature film from the back of a van, because the Saudis don't allow women to work in the streets. The interviewer kept asking her about women's rights in Saudi Arabia. 'I'm an artist, not an activist,' she said. She just wanted to tell a story, not make a big deal out of her oppression. I think it's an important distinction to make. Not everyone has to take a stand. I'm at the checkout, keeping an eye out for the kids. Leo barrels towards me, a box of Froot-Loops under his arm. I shake my head. He begins the campaign, arms flapping, hopping from one foot to the other. I tell him to help me load the groceries onto the counter. My chest feels weird.

Tight. My heart starts to flutter. I can't breathe properly. I stop loading the groceries and take a minute. Slow my breath, stare at the floor. I'm back. I keep loading the groceries, but I feel trapped. I need to get back to the car right now. I could leave the groceries and the children and just make an exit. They will find their way back to the car. I don't leave. I stay and pay for the groceries. The girl at the checkout looks fuzzy. The noticeboard looks fuzzy. I can hear the bleep of every item as it's scanned. The kids emerge.

'What's wrong, Mum?' asks Layla.

'I'm okay. Let's go. Quickly.'

By the time we get back to the car, everything is normal again. I feel fine.

The following week it happens again, after work. I'm cooking dinner and the boys are fighting over the remote. I feel my heart start first, then the breathing stops, then the feeling of being trapped, then the fuzzy walls. I turn off the stove and go into my room, and get under the doona. I am breathing in loud rasps and my head is spinning. I grab my phone and call Borhan. He picks up.

'Hey,' he says warily (the puppy fight is still fresh).

'I need you to come here and look after the kids. The boys are fighting, and something is wrong with me,' I say in starts, drawing in breath like a steel anchor.

'Do you need an ambulance?' he asks, alarmed.

'No. I just need you to come here.'

'I'm on my way.'

Five minutes later he barrels through the front door, and yells at the boys to stop fighting. I hear his footsteps moving quickly through the house. He knocks gently on the door of my room as he pushes it open.

'What's going on?' he asks, sitting on the edge of the bed.

'I think I'm having a panic attack. I can't breathe,' I say, sitting up, rasping air in, in quick starts.

He grips my shoulders calmly. 'Slowly,' he says, breathing deeply. 'Look at me, Seets. Breathe with me, slowly. Match my breath.'

I try and copy his breathing. In and out, slowly. I make my diaphragm obey, pulling the reins on it to mimic the pace of his. It's very effective. We have been here before. We have birthed three children together. We've held hands through the blood and shit and vomit, through the gurgled cries and the torn flesh. In moments of pain or terror, Borhan is the calmest and kindest of men. As my breathing slows and the world regains a dull clarity, I realise his hands are on my bare shoulders and his breath is in my face and here we are – expats returned to a war-torn homeland. The buildings have crumbled and the landscape is pock-marked and ravaged by the fray, and we could never live here again, we could never survive it. But everything is so familiar, my insides ache.

'I don't think I was mean about the dog thing,' I say, perversely choosing this moment of compassion to reopen the wound.

'You were,' he replies wearily. 'Your tone was cold.'

'You just read it as cold. If I read it out to you, it would sound warm.'

'It doesn't matter, anyway. I've already bought one.'

1962. Tsangdhar Mountain Range. The Himalayas.

The Chinese had been trying to conquer the outpost for two months, but the Indians were fighting valiantly to retain control over the crucial mountain range. If Tsangdhar fell, then the border war contesting control of the Aksai Chin, a white stone plateau at the top of the world, would no doubt tip in favour of the Chinese. Early that morning, Squadron Leader Vinod Sehgal flew by chopper from Zimithang, to rescue the wounded and restore communication with the base. He had not yet returned. Nobody had returned.

Squadron Leader Sochindronath (Satto) Williams had just arrived in Zimithang, from Gauhati, where he was delivering supplies. Ammunition. Food. Blankets. Bandages.

The commander was waiting for him. 'Williams. Your order is to fly immediately to Tsangdhar. Vinod Sehgal has not returned. Find out what happened, and report back.'

In Gauhati, Satto had seen the Dakota which had just returned from a supply dropping mission over Tsangdhar. It was peppered with bullet holes. Word had not yet reached Zimithang that the mountain outpost had been taken by the Chinese. The commander was uninformed. Satto would of course inform him and declare the mission untenable, if it wasn't for the crushing fact that Vinod Sehgal was his trusted confidant. More than that, he was his best friend. He had to find him.

'Yes, sir,' he said with a salute, and made his way to the launch zone.

Coasting over the Tsangdhar range in his Bell 47G-3 chopper, Satto could see no signs of life. The usual smoke signal over the outpost was not adrift. He flew in a circle over the valley, dwarfed by the mountainous peaks that surrounded it. An eerie, cold silence floated in the white air. The Namka Chu stream iced and bubbled its way at a herding pace through the craggy gorge below.

Suddenly, an ear-splitting barrage of bullets pummelled the helicopter from all sides. Metal venom. The valley which a moment ago was so still and quiet was suddenly resounding with the crack and blow of machine-gun fire from all around. The Bell's cockpit instruments were shattered. The oil pressure indicator, or what was left of it, showed 'zero'.

Satto felt a tearing of the flesh of his upper back, like fire to a cut. He instantly executed a corkscrew manoeuvre and dived out of the cirque. The engine could seize at any moment, that much was clear. Below, waiting for his crash landing, was ice, bare rocks and the Chinese army.

Satto was familiar with the route and the updraughts and downdraughts. He hugged the edge of the cliff where there was a good updraught. Fortunately, the damaged engine continued to fire and lifted the helicopter over the last ridge before seizing up. Satto auto-rotated down the other side of the valley.

A small clearing came into view. There it was. He knew it. He had remembered his bearings. Boulders strewn top and bottom, the roaring gorge to the left, and a young tree to the right, Satto would need to auto-rotate tightly enough to land in the middle. Which he did, crash landing just inches from the gorge.

Satto Williams had not always flown rescue helicopters. He began his career on spitfires. Bombers. His superiors saw him as the perfect officer – unquestioned loyalty, a bright mind, a pole-vault record holder and diving and swimming champion, with physical ability second to none. He was also a man of great principle, which meant that when he became a Bahá'í, Satto knew he could no longer drop bombs from planes or shoot bullets out of guns. He approached his command and said that his new faith teaches men to love all people regardless of race or colour, to 'see no one as their enemy, or as wishing them ill, but think of all humankind as their friends' and that as a result of this, 'conflict and contention are in no wise permitted'. His superiors were agape, but fortunately, their respect for him as an officer prompted them to find a creative solution. Rather than being discharged, Satto was transferred to search and rescue.

Now, his helicopter was crushed and mangled, and he was bleeding from the back and the mouth. After making a quick assessment of his person, Satto ascertained that, through God's mercy, the bullet had not pierced his lungs, and none of his bones had been broken. He was relatively put together, considering what had happened.

It took three hours, surrounded by trees, creepers, boulders and rocky ravines, for him to trek back to his base. In that time in the freezing, wooded valley, with the threat of death lurking around every crag, Satto made two decisions. If he made it back alive, he would immediately and certainly write to the most beautiful girl he had ever met, and ask her to marry him. And, when her belly swelled and she gave birth to his first son, they would name him Vinod.

1988. Toowoomba.

Bent into half in downward dog, I look through my legs at my Uncle Satto. His neatly clipped and meticulously combed beard and moustache are snow-white against his brown skin. His white yoga singlet and stirruped pants are perfectly pressed. The five or six students, barefoot on mats in his home yoga studio, are all folded like triangles, in downward dog. Uncle Satto looks at me, his face a portrait of composure, and winks. I know what's coming. My favourite part of the class. He puts his head to the ground, and with his palms pressed to the floor, he walks his feet forward towards his nose. The students dutifully copy. Then, he bends his knees and pushes both legs up into the air with controlled ease until his body is straight like an arrow, toes pointing to the ceiling. He is standing on his head. Perfectly balanced. Serene. A yogi through and through.

A murmur ripples through the room. The students are in all states of bent and wobbly confusion, trying to stand on their heads. I giggle. Satto breaks into a wide grin. This is when they realise their serious, sculpted yoga teacher, is just having them on.

'Come on!' he says, his accent thick. 'It's easy. Children can do it!'

On cue, I scooch up next to my uncle and push myself up into a wobbly headstand, my skinny legs as straight as chopsticks, my bare toes pointing upwards as gracefully as I can manage.

'Ta dah!' I announce breathily to the class. It's charming. I'm a seven-year-old with two missing front teeth. I'm adorable. Everyone laughs. Uncle Satto lets his legs down and comes to a standing position with the elegance of an Olympic diver. He presses his palms together and bows 'namaste' to his students, who return their thanks in kind. The class is finished.

I somersault out of my headstand and race to the kitchen, where my Aunty Irie is laying out lunch.

'It's finished!' I announce with a gap-toothed whistle. 'They're coming!'

'Sita-koo, come. Taste this.'

She puts a neatly cut triangle of pistachio and rose halwa in my mouth. It tastes like a creamy flower.

'What's your score?'

'Ten out of ten!' I sing.

'Now some kulfi?' she offers.

I take a small bowl out of her hand and dip a spoon into the saffron and almond frozen dessert. It is transcendent. Eleven out of ten. Nobody cooks like my Aunty Irie, or looks so perfect doing it.

She's wearing a wine-coloured long skirt and a white, boat-neck blouse. A flowery apron over it all. She's small and pillowy, with diamonds in her olive nose and ears, and her hair in a loose bun. She wears little house slippers and spoils me like nobody else on this earth. Not even Dolly.

I spend hours in front of her bedroom mirror, trying on her saris and her jewellery. Long strands of freshwater pearls, gold and silver necklaces in every length, bracelets of amethyst and turquoise and rose-gold, silver anklets with bells, earrings that look like shimmering baskets, or bunches of delicate golden berries, or shining suns. Irie has an emerald ring, hugged by tiny diamonds. A ruby moon pendant. And my favourite, a gold and pearl brooch in the shape of a bird, with a blue sapphire eye. I pick it up and pin it to the checked collar of my school uniform.

'My sweetie was a very famous pilot. We always had lovely things,' Irie says, reclining on her bed, sipping tea, popping pistachio nuts and buds of carob chocolate into her mouth. 'Rehana Sultan gave me that brooch. Oof oof, Sita-koo, she was so beautiful. No wonder she was a film star. Her face. Her eyes! Round, like moons. Just like Vinod's. Oh, she loved my Vinod. She would pull him onto her lap and kiss his cheeks and they would stare at one another with their big eyes.' Irie laughs like an imp. 'We would have jewellery parties with all the things your Uncle Satt-Satt would bring us back from his trips to New York . . .' then, with a sigh . . . 'I was very rich.'

Completely under her spell, I pull out a pair of earrings that look like strawberry shortcakes, clusters of tiny pearls and candy-pink gems in golden cups.

'Those were from Mona Anand. We lived next door to her in the Bel Air apartments, in Bombay. Air India's international pilots were like gods then. I was in luxury. Her husband Dev Anand was a big star, you know . . .'

And on and on it went. She talked. I listened. She let me wrap and adorn myself in her saris and jewels, like a tiny Indian princess.

Once, in the back of her oaken closet, I found a box with a carved lid. Inside was a smaller box, maroon and gold. Inside the smaller box was a medal with a star on it. I pulled it out and pinned it to my uniform, and then I wore it out into the back-yard, where my uncle was potting succulents in his greenhouse.

'Uncle Satto! What are you doing?' I called in a singing voice, skipping over the timber verandah trellised with grape and passionfruit vines, down a small set of stairs into their wide, circular garden. The trees were dropping burnt-orange and garnet leaves. The grass was covered with them, crunchy and scalloped.

'My Pretty-Mittie! Come. Let's rake the leaves now,' Satto said, emerging from the greenhouse with two rakes in tow. That was our favourite pastime. Raking the leaves together.

'Oh, I see . . .' he said, stopping short, looking at my collar.

He was still and stared for a moment. I looked down at the medal.

'I think we had better put this one away, Pretty-Mittie,' he said in a soft voice.

'What is it?'

'It's very old. Almost thirty years now . . .'

Satto gently unpinned the navy and orange ribbon from my collar, held the medal carefully in his palm, and walked back into the house. He remembered shaking the warm hand of India's first prime minister, Shri Jawaharlal Nehru, who presented him with it. It was the Vir Chakra. Awarded by the Indian military for acts of conspicuous gallantry, and bravery of the highest order.

Eleven months ago.

'Sita, where are you?'

It's Fari.

'I'm walking, Ma.'

Not strictly a lie.

'Where are you walking?'

'Just doing some exercise.'

Again, not a lie that would stick in my throat. There's an element of cross-fit. I have to negotiate small dogs, large people, and tall tables and chairs to get to the Regatta front bar.

'Where are the kids?'

'It's Monday night, Ma.'

'So what?'

'So they've been with Borhan every Monday night for five years.'

Fari is not sure how divorce works. I've tried explaining it. Once I even drew up a table for her. Diagrams. Sock-puppets. Nights with me/nights with Borhan. She prefers to pretend I am always at home with my children.

'I gotta go, Ma.'

'Love you, baby. Have some dinner, okay?'

'Yep. Love you. Bye.'

I hang up and order two glasses of Shaw and Smith sauvignon blanc and a bowl of fries. It's date three with the actor, and I've arrived early. Again. The bar is lined with collar-tie men knocking off. They order beer from cut bartenders with no apparent hipster leanings. Not a handle-bar moustache or a sleeve-tattoo in sight. The Regatta is not how I remember it. I spent the occasional night here in the late nineties, with friends who stayed at University of Queensland colleges. They studied things like physiotherapy and biomedical engineering and law. They dated drunk grammar-school types in jerseys, deck shoes and Canterbury shorts. Boys called Chris and Tom and Woodsy and Hendo. I look out the front bay windows of the pub. The four lanes of Coronation Drive heave with after-work traffic. The twinkling skin of the river is copper-gold. I realise the difference is time. Not the passage of time. The actual time. It's not 11pm, it's five. Chris and Tom and Woodsy and Hendo are still busy stocking up on frangers at the 7-Eleven.

The wine is expensive but I don't want to look like I always order the cheapest glass on the menu. Not that I think there's any shame in ordering the house white, but I don't want to show my hand just yet – if ever. I've abandoned the Joan Baez boho frock/faux-fur vibe in favour of a more streamlined look, in the hope that a classy sweater, pedal pushers and ballet flats will save me from myself. No more artless I love yous or that was delightfuls from me. From now on, I will be a mysterious and alluring chameleon. A shape-shifting seductress. More Audrey Hepburn, less Lucille Ball. More Baroness, less Maria von Trapp.

I carry the wine and the order number out to the terrace. I select a high-table accompanied by two awkwardly teetering stools.

Anthony arrives. He makes a quick assessment of the situation and deduces that we should move to a lower table on the Sylvan Road side – a less elevated dynamic will make for more intimate connection.

Wowsers.

There's a cursory breeze. An orange glow. I sit down, cross my legs elegantly, lean back, and take a small sip. This whole 'less elevated' caper is all right. Anthony asks me about my writing. I tell him I've had a small piece published. I tell him it's nothing. He disagrees. I tell him I'm trying to get a book deal, but I can't imagine ever getting one. We talk about the work. He's interested. I'm a bit embarrassed but I try not to let it show. We talk about it some more. I ask him what he feels about God as a concept. He doesn't subscribe. He's not a fan of organised religion, but each to their own. His particular life ethos boils down to 'don't be a cunt to people'. Outside of that, it's the work he's interested in. His work and his boy.

The chips arrive. Why is Brisbane so obsessed with aioli? I ask the waiter for tomato sauce. The baroness is slipping. The couple next to us is talking about their kids. It must be 'date night'. I hitch up the sleeves of my sweater and take a chip.

Anthony is quiet for a moment.

'This could be really great, you know?' he finally says.

'How do you mean?'

'Well I guess . . . you've got your bullshit over there . . . I've got my bullshit over here . . .'

'And in the middle of all that . . .' I add.

'. . . we just have a beautiful romance?' Anthony finishes.

I look down and our hands have been clasped across the table for the last half hour.

'That is exactly what I want.'

'It's not the worst way for things to go, I reckon. You know, you have kids with someone, it doesn't work out, you split up. It's really tough, but you compartmentalise all that. You've got your kids now, and they're incredible. Then you meet someone new – and you can just have a wonderful time, and that's all you have to do. Just enjoy each other. I mean, despite what we've come through to get here, this could be a lovely place to be.'

'It is. We may have found the secret to happiness.'

I feel emancipated. It's my time. I've done fifteen years in domestic suburgatory. School lunches. Soccer canteen duty. Footy training. Jazz band concerts. Fetes. I've cooked nine thousand pots of spaghetti bolognaise, washed eleven hundred loads of laundry, mopped up vomit and pee and poop, stuck band-aids on bloody knees, ironed uniforms, traipsed the aisles of Officeworks ticking stationery off a twenty-page booklist with a toddler hanging from my leg, and none of that, none, is going to be part of whatever this is. A lovely fling, a sweet little affair – whatever. I'm taking Andy's advice and not allowing my mind to take this from me. I won't label it, overthink it or make it a thing. I'll enjoy the simple, placeless pleasures of talking, laughing, strolling, kissing.

This is no post-divorce *Eat, Pray, Love.* No one in the real world can leave their children and their job for twelve months to roam the globe eating pasta, praying to a guru, and romancing Brazilian jewel traders. But everyone can have one small thing, can't they? Just one. One sacred little secret that can't be touched. One bright star under which to whisper in the wee hours: I did that. It happened.

After a few wines, a mushroom pizza and a parmy, we walk along the river. The night is clear and the city is lit. We talk about our favourite books. *Brother of the More Famous Jack. The Corrections. Monkey Grip.* Our favourite movies. *No Country for Old Men. Adaptation. The Big Lebowski.* We make out on a bench by the river. We're interrupted by night-walkers with small dogs and a call from my ex-husband. We make out some more. There is groping. Pressing. Stirring of loins. My mind is an eddy and my heart is full and my body feels unreal. Glow-heavy, moon-bright and about to burst.

At 11.45pm we kiss goodbye. I'm frustrated. He's frustrated. I'm laughing. He's smiling. We're like school kids who can't get to third base but are stoked we got to second. It is marvellous and terrible. I take an Uber home to my empty house. I swap the ballet flats, pedal pushers and classy sweater for Ugg boots and a faded Nike t-shirt. I pull a cigarette from the back of my jewellery box, lie on the trampoline, and look up through the leaves of the poinciana to the black sky. My limbs like a starfish. There's Orion's belt. Three stars twinkling in a line through a gap in the laced foliage. I put the dart to my kiss-swollen lips and suck at the flame.

Ping.

My phone interrupts. It's him. My beautiful, unsullied romance. My one secret thing. My bright star.

Bit toey now.

Tell me about it.

2004. Weipa.

Mona sat on the steps of the community centre and scratched her ankle. It was hot, and the sea breeze had blown a swarm of midges her way. She didn't believe that there was no job for her in Weipa, like the lady had said. She didn't even want to be paid. John made enough money for two families to live comfortably. She just wanted to help, to serve her God, to do something for people who needed something done for them. She didn't care what colour those people were. She wasn't politically motivated to help; she didn't see herself as a saviour of any kind, or a do-gooder. She just wanted to use her two arms and two legs in an act of service, rather than die of boredom.

John was out fishing. The sky-water of the Gulf teemed with barramundi, mangrove jack, fingermark bream, giant threadfin salmon, grunter, snub-nosed dart, big eye trevally and black marlin. Every type of swimming feast was there waiting for the bait. Sometimes you didn't even need a worm to catch your dinner, you simply lowered a hook off the jetty and pulled. John wasn't jetty fishing, he was out on his boat, angling for a narrow-barred Spanish mackerel. When he caught one Mona would slice through it whole, cutting cylindrical chunks of luminescent silver-grey skin, fine bone and pink flesh. She would salt and fry it in oil, sprinkled with turmeric and ground coriander, mustard seeds and lime. They would eat it with white rice and pickles.

Mona was seventy-two. Her body was thick but healthy. Her mind was sharp. She had never been less interested in her age. The only pain she felt was the burn of impatience. Her shop on Thursday Island – 'Mona's Bazaar' was wildly successful – it was becoming an institution. She had more money now than ever before, not that she counted it, but the woman at the community centre had looked at her like she was worthless. Fit only to weave baskets by the sea, or chop beans out the back of the fish-hut kitchen. Mona searched through her handbag for a strong peppermint to suck while she thought of what to do.

From out of the briny bush opposite the community centre, a group of skeletal boys emerged. If it wasn't for the sound of their slurred chatter, Mona would have thought they were ghosts. She watched the ragged group float by like hazed zombies. There were ten boys, probably no older than sixteen, some as young as eleven or twelve. They were wafting and stumbling down the street, swearing and pushing each other like old drunks. Some were shirtless, and Mona could see their rib bones wearing their skin like paint. As they came closer, the acrid tang of petrol hit her nostrils.

Mona got up and walked back into the centre.

'Who are those skinny boys across the street?' she asked the lady who had just sent her away. Her name badge optimistically said: 'Hi! I'm Angie.'

'Them skinny boys are sniffers. They no good,' Angie said, without looking up from her paperwork.

'What it means? Sniffers?' Mona asked.

Angie put her pen down impatiently and took her glasses off, looking up sour. 'They sniff petrol. Gets 'em high. Makes 'em forget they ain't eaten anything. Then they wreck the place, the little bastards.' She muttered that last bit, taking up her pen again and continuing to fill out her forms.

'Can I work with these sniffers?' asked Mona after a moment.

Angie laughed heartily. 'You can do whatever you want with them sniffers, love. You go right ahead . . .'

Mona had a 1993 Toyota Camry in what was once a deep magenta. The back seat was large enough to hold a slab of cast iron from an old barbecue, six red house bricks, several packets of thin beef sausages from the IGA, and four loaves of white bread. She also bought a few bottles of supermarket brand cola and orange soda, a tub of yellow margarine, and a bottle of Heinz tomato sauce. Then she drove her makeshift barbecue to where she had seen the boys appear out of the paperbark trees.

Leaving the car parked at the edge of the scrub, Mona dragged the iron and the bricks through the bush, past the mangroves to where the trees met the sand. On the beach she made a small dugout, lugged some driftwood and bush into it and laid bricks on either side. Then she set the tinder ablaze, and dropped the iron slab onto the bricks with a clatter.

The sea wind made sure the fire held the kindling while Mona fetched her supplies from the car, and collected a small but reassuring pile of dry wood to keep the cooker going. Mona knew hunger, but she also knew that the feeling of not having enough to eat was the poor brother of not having enough to drink. After asking round town, Darrel Meeney, John's short, bald friend at the council office in Napranum, told her that inhaling petrol fumes from a rag made you feel momentarily euphoric, but it burnt your throat dry and stuck the saliva to your gums like white glue. Bega Crosser, her neighbour, told her that the sniffing makes the gang boys happy, and then it makes 'em fight and scrape with anything that moves. It burns out their insides slowly. Shrinks their hearts. Bega was a nurse so she would know.

Mona had seen poverty in India. Emaciated opium addicts and spindly beggars and children with wrists like fingers. The cause of all of it was hate, greed and power in the hands of people who hungered for it. She tore a piece of bread in half and stuffed it in her mouth, chewing slowly as she scooped a forkful of margarine onto the hot plate. It sizzled. She peeled open the sausages and tossed them on, pushing them around with some tongs. The smell of crackling beef skin and butter floated out over the coast and blew back into the bush. A flock of Pacific gulls dipped in and out of the sea, fishing for their breakfast. Squawking and chattering over the blue.

The Gulf water is clear and deep and bright all at once. It's tempting, but swim out there and your hands and feet will be croc food. If you make it past the crocs, the sharks will be only too happy to eat out your heart. Mona scratched her ankles and dug her heels into the yellow sand. She wondered what these skinny sniffer gang-boys had to sniff for. She would find out.

As predicted, they materialised from the bush in ones and twos. Mona hummed to herself. A Persian chant, low and soft. She called them over with an upwards flick of her chin, pushing the snags gently around the hotplate. The fire crackled and breathed. Mona held up a bottle of cola. A wisp of a boy approached her and took it from her hand, twisting it open with a fizzy pop. She ignored him. He blinked his sunken eyes, took a slug and passed it around the four other boys.

'Wan' 'em?' Mona asked in pidgin, tapping the bag of bread with her fork. 'Take 'em,' she said, her eyes out to sea.

The boys descended on the bread and took slices, looking eagerly at the sausages on the grill. Before long, around sixteen more kids had wandered out of the scrub. Mona began passing out the meat, one slim stick of beef at a time. 'Them hot. You wait 'em cool down,' she said, as she squeezed the sauce out onto their bread and laid a sausage on each.

The boys ate like tiny starving drunks, sitting in the sand of the beach. Mona threw another round on and twisted open the orange soda. It all went. The meat, the bread, the sauce, the drinks.

When it was finished she tapped the makeshift barbecue with her fork and said, 'You leave this one here. I come back tomorrow. Cook for you.'

Each day for two weeks Mona did the same trip to the beach. Each day the sniffers came to eat and drink. At the end of the first week they began to talk to Mona, and at the end of the second she began to talk back.

'What your name? Why you comin' here?'

'I comin' cos you got to eat. My name is Mona.'

'We gonna call you Mama Joe.'

'Okay. You call me Mama Joe. I keep comin'.'

Mona told the boys what bald Darrel and nurse Bega had said about what they were doing. She told them that they would die from the sniffing if they didn't stop. She told them that their insides would shrivel up and their hearts would stop and they would be no better than the sausages she was frying. She told them that she loved them. She told them that they were her kids and she wouldn't forget to feed them. And she never forgot.

At the end of the first month, Mona's car tyre went flat on her drive from Napranum to Weipa. She drove it sloppily the rest of the way and parked near the trees again. After feeding the boys, she returned to the council building and spoke to the night watchman, Bob Hoskey. Hoskey was a skinny fella with a neck like a plucked chook and yellow teeth from too many cigarettes and cups of cheap black coffee. But, he was all right. You couldn't leave cars out around here, so Mona asked him to put hers in his garage overnight so that it wasn't stolen or stripped. Bob agreed to drive it to his place before he started his shift.

Early the next day, Mona and John returned to Weipa with a spare tyre. They went to Hoskey's place to pick up the car. It wasn't in his garage. John banged on the door of his house. Bob emerged, bleary eyed.

'Where's Mona's car, Bob?' John asked.

Hoskey rubbed his face with one hand, and scratched his arse. The sun was too bright. John was far too loud. 'I couldn't go near ya wife's bloody car,' he muttered, half asleep. 'Them sniffers wouldn't let me touch the damn thing, would they? Surrounded it like a pack of dingoes. Looked at me like I was the thief. It's right where ya left it.'

When John and Mona arrived at the Camry, it was untouched.

1996. Toowoomba.

I make my way up the back stairs, with my schoolbag slung over one shoulder, running a hand through my cropped bob. It was a shitty day at the swimming carnival. I had my period – for real, this time, not just as an excuse not to swim. I approached the sports mistress after roll call and explained the problem. She gave me a disappointed look, turned me to face all the girls in my house, about 150 of them, and with her hands on my shoulders she addressed us: 'Ladies, listening please!' The girls simmered to silence. 'Having your period is no excuse not to swim today! This is the nineties. There are ways and means of maintaining yourself so that you can participate fully in the sports program. Surely, you all know what to do.'

Jesus. It was embarrassing.

My face flushed, and as soon as she released her grip on my shoulders I sat down right where I was, hoping to be consumed by the floorboards. My friends Rachel and Beck shuffled across the room to meet me while Mistress went on mustering the troops, her white shorts flush against her tanned thighs.

'What the fuck?' hissed Rachel.

'Oh my god, she's such a bitch,' said Beck, putting her arm around my shoulder.

'Do you guys have any tampons?' I asked, under my breath.

I was fifteen when I got my period. It was a nail-biting wait for womanhood. While all my friends talked about being 'on their rags' or 'surfing the crimson wave' I pretended I was lucky I didn't have to deal with the hassle. But I was desperate for it to happen. Desperate. When I finally started bleeding I was so relieved I cried. I told Fari and she bought me a packet of supermarket brand maxi pads with no wings and no fuss. 'Surfboards', we used to call them. My sister, Lisa, came home one weekend and saw that the sanitary pad situation at Bridge Street was dire, so she went to town and bought me a cute pack of individually wrapped Libra pads, with flowers on the wrapping and wings to attach them to my underpants. 'Wear two pairs of undies,' she said. 'I'll tell Ma not to buy the surfboards anymore.'

We never bought tampons. I had never used a tampon. I don't think Fari was morally opposed to them – she probably didn't even know what they were, but I could hardly counter a public accusation of menstruational immaturity with, 'Well, my mummy doesn't buy me tampons', could I?

Beck had some in her sports bag and she slipped three into my palm. They were long and thin. They must be the applicator ones, I thought. I had no idea how to use them, but I took them from her and zipped them into the pocket of my skirt. We filed into the indoor swimming complex, the smell of chlorine thick in the humid air, the rush of pool water sloshing into whitewashed drains. Chatter echoed. Most of my friends were already in the stands, crinkling lolly wrappers and chip packets. Rachel and Beck had gone to the vending machine. Lydia, Brona and Kat (the eager, athletic ones) were pushing their shiny hair into talcum-powder filled latex caps and stretching to warm up. I waved at Annabel (funny girl, dreadful swimmer) but she was too busy sucking on a Chupa Chup and staring at the water with withered contempt to notice. Mr Harcourt was testing the starter gun, his long knee socks pulled up neatly, shorts crisp, silver whistle shining. I avoided him and made my way to the changing rooms.

Sitting on the toilet bowl, I unwrapped one of the contraptions and stared at it, turning it over in my fingers.

It was two plastic tubes slotted together, with a cotton string hanging from the end. I figured I had to insert one end and use the other end to push in the tampon, but I wasn't sure. There were no instructions. I tested the first one in my lap, pushing the smaller tube slowly upwards. The tampon popped out the other end and onto my thighs. Bingo. I put all the parts back into my pocket and tore open a fresh packet. With my skirt and undies around my ankles, I reached down. I had no idea what I was doing, and I couldn't see because my shirt was in the way. It hurt. Fumbling, I shoved the hem of my shirt into my mouth, and tried again, peering downwards, pushing a little bit harder with the tube. I could feel the plastic scraping my insides, and a weird burning sensation. I pulled the applicator out gently and held it in front of me to see how far in it had gone, like checking the oil level in an engine. Blood dripped onto my skirt. Shit. I quickly wiped it with toilet paper and tried again. My shirt was wet with saliva and I was sweating. The change room was humid and damp. Hedging my bets, I held the tube steady and pushed the end of the applicator to release the tampon. It slipped out and fell into the toilet bowl with a soft splash. Shiiiiit. I threw the applicator into the sanitary bin, wiped my hands with toilet paper, and opened the last packet.

The room was filling up with girls. Their chatter was making me nervous. It would be only minutes before someone smacked the toilet door and told me to hurry up. My hand was shaking slightly as I tried a different angle this time. After a bit of wiggling I thought I had it. Yes! I quickly pushed to release the tampon. There was a stab of pain, but no splash. It was in. Elated, I chucked the applicator into the sanitary bin and stood up. Something wasn't right. It didn't feel overly painful but I couldn't move without wincing slightly. I sat back down. Balancing on the toilet seat with one buttock, I lifted up a leg and braced it on the toilet roll holder, leant back, and peered down between my legs. Half the tampon and the white string were sticking out. Shit. Shit. Shit. I tried pushing it gently with my finger, but it hurt so much I had to bite my bottom lip to keep from crying out. Fuck this. Fuck swimming. I yanked on the string and dropped the last tampon into the bowl. My eyes filled with tears.

The rest of the day moved in tandem with its beginning. That is to say, it did not improve.

When I got back to Bridge Street, I flung my bag down on the pile of shoes on the landing and walked straight to the fridge, yanking it open and staring zombie-like at the contents. Grandma called to me from her recliner chair in the family room, 'Sita! You home, Baba? Eat some toast.'

I shut the fridge and went to her. Her swollen feet were up on the footrest and she was thumbing through a *Women's Weekly*, plastic-framed reading spectacles perched on the end of her nose. Seeing me, she dropped the glasses and let them hang from the beaded lanyard around her neck. Without saying anything, I sat on the wide armrest and slid down slowly until I was squashed into the recliner with her, my feet touching hers, my head resting back on the cushioned headrest.

'What is it?' she asked, tapping my thigh with her warm, crinkled hand. We fit together like sardines. I leant my head against her shoulder and turned in to hug her soft middle. She wrapped her arm around me and patted me gently. 'What? Say now. What happened?' she murmured.

'Nothing. We had the swimming carnival today,' I mumbled into her shoulder.

'Carnival? Like fun and games?'

'No. Races. Like the Olympics.'

'You didn't win any races?' she asked, surprised. 'Did you want to win the races and you didn't?'

I didn't say anything.

'So what?' she announced boldly. 'You are the best swimmer. You swim the best in our family. So what you didn't win? Next time you will win.'

None of this is even remotely true. I am not a good swimmer. Certainly not the best swimmer. My swimming style could be described as survival-stroke meets flappy-bird. But my grandmother thought I was the best at everything, and even if I wasn't, she thought I could be if I wanted to.

Explaining what really happened would be pointless. She definitely didn't know what a tampon was, nor did she understand the evangelical devotion to sports fostered in Australian high schools. I didn't bother to correct her, I just inhaled her scent. Talcum powder, coffee and peppermints. I melted into her shoulder and cried a little bit.

'Areh, areh, areh,' she tutted with alarm, wiping my cheeks, kissing my head, patting my thigh.

She pulled out the grey leather wallet that was always wedged between the seat cushion and the armrest.

Every week, John took Dolly's pension money out of the bank and gave it to her in cash. She tucked it into a white handkerchief which she kept in her wallet. She used most of it to bankroll her grandchildren's whims, and what was left was spent on sweets, antacids, magazines and lotto tickets.

'You want twenty dollar?' she asked solemnly.

I laughed. And cried. 'All right,' I smiled, sniffing.

She pulled out a tightly folded red note, pressed it into my palm, and closed my fingers over it like a drug deal.

'Quickly – zip it up in your pocket,' she whispered, clicking shut the clasp of her wallet and stuffing it back down into the seat.

She pulled the *Women's Weekly* open. 'Look how beautiful is Diana. She's leaving Prince Charles, see . . .' she tutted and tapped her finger on the picture of Camilla Parker Bowles giving the Prince of Wales a sideways glance. 'Look at this witch!' She read the headline one word at a time, running her finger under it. 'There were three of us in the marriage so it was a bit crowded . . .' she tutted again.

I put my head back and closed my eyes. The spring breeze and the smell of clover floated through the open window and touched my face.

2016. Brisbane.

Aunty Irie has heard the news of mine and Borhan's split. My phone rings aggressively. Her still-beautiful face shines out at me from the sunlit, windowed kitchen of her apartment in the Czech Republic. It's evening here, midday there. She's preparing a luncheon for her English conversation class, a group of Czech ladies in their early sixties, learning to speak English. Accomplished women. One ex-judge, one lawyer, several teachers.

'What are you cooking, Aunty?' I ask, in an attempt to sideline what I know is coming.

She ignores me. 'Sita-koo, what happened?'

This question. Will I ever stop hearing it? I'm lying in bed. I've just got the kids to sleep. Weariness is raked over my face.

'It's a long story, Aunty.'

'Look at you! Like a ghost! What do you need? Money? Of course, you need money . . . where is Fari?'

She tuts and props her phone up on the window ledge, ducking out of the frame for a moment.

'Ma is in Toowoomba. She's been here with me, Aunty. Don't worry.'

She's back in view, with a mortar bowl. She crushes a star anise and some cardamom pods into it with the marble pestle. Her elbow is raised high.

'Worry? I never worry. I pray to God! And when I can't pray, I eat.' She cackles, then looks up urgently. 'Have you eaten? You look thin.'

It's my turn to laugh. 'What are you gonna do? Press the biryani through the phone?'

'Watch me,' she says, smiling. 'Oh my darling. My Sita-koo. I wish I was there . . . You need money, don't you? I'm sending you some. Today. I'll have Jordan do it on the computer.'

'You really don't have to do that, Aunty . . .'

'Stop arguing with me. It's done.'

'Okay, okay. Thank you. I love you.'

'I love you more.'

'What are you cooking for your ladies?'

She calls them her 'ladies' because she doesn't know any of their names. Instead, she refers to them by profession. 'My judge', 'my lawyer', 'my teacher'. She speaks not a word of Czech, but uses her grandchildren to translate.

'Lamb curry. My judge loves lamb. She's used to the good life, like me. You know how hard it is to get proper lamb here? Among these thieves?'

Anyone who charges over the Australian market price for lamb is considered a criminal of the highest order. Supply and demand chains mean nothing to Irie.

'Aunty, they were communists not too long ago . . . they can't help the price of things like lamb.'

'Don't be ridiculous! They can and they should.'

I laugh and she smiles . . . 'Good girl. Be happy, my sunshine. That's what my sweetie would say if he was here. He loved you so much, Sita-koo.'

'I know, Aunty.'

'And you know what I'm going to say, don't you?'

I nod, but she can't see me. She's pottered away to stir the curry. She calls from the stove, 'Nobody ever got anything they wanted by sitting quietly and waiting for it!'

'Yes, Aunty,' I say.

Her face pops back into the frame. Wisps of sweaty hair are stuck to her temples.

'Don't let the world take you for a ride, my Sita. You take the world for a ride.'

The room feels bigger all of a sudden. Filled with air.

The next day, there is five thousand dollars in my bank account.

2018. Brisbane.

I stare at the fetid pool, swarming with mosquitos. My back and neck are bent, my phone is under my ear. I'm too tall to stand upright under the house. I listen to the number ring out and dial again. The kids are around and about. Leo is collecting gumnuts and little weed-flowers, Layla is inside, hiding from the mozzies. Will is tightrope walking along the cement edge of what has now become a small, rancid swimming pool. He's chucked a bunch of stuff in there. A plastic Ironman with a chewed foot floats in the corner. A Tiny Teddy plastic packet blows across the surface. Some Lego bricks and a bruised mandarin bob up and down in the muck.

There is a weird dugout under The Shack, and it fills with water. Since the summer rain, it's been filling up regularly.

It's not draining dry or evaporating quickly enough to keep the mosquitos at bay. I've called the agency six times. They are trying to get a solution from the owner, who seems to think it's fine to let the water sit there until it dries out 'naturally'.

The receptionist picks up and I begin again. Explaining what's happened, explaining why it's unacceptable to have a pool of warm, stagnant water under your timber, post-war cottage.

'It's not just the smell. My kids are being eaten alive by mosquitos. My youngest can't play outside by himself. He could drown. I'm sure the owners don't want a five-year-old to drown.'

'I'm soooo sorry to hear that,' says Jess, the clicky-clacky front desker. She takes an audible, dramatic breath of sympathy. In and out. 'We are absolutely working with the owners of the property to resolve this ish-shew.'

Oh my god, it will never be dry.

The weird pool isn't the only problem with The Shack. The shower leaks, the back-door lock sticks, and the kids' rooms have dense crim-safe grilles on the windows, giving the home an air of penitentiary-chic and stopping the light from coming in. The neighbours are uni students. They party on weeknights and burn shit in the backyard on the weekends. They swear at pitch. They spit. Last week, one of them peed on my front fence at 11pm, before hopping in an Uber I can only presume was going to the Valley. I know this because my bedroom window faces the street and is close enough to the front fence for me to hear his pee hit, and trickle. Oh, and his loud announcement: 'Hold up, bro. I'm havin' a slash.'

There is also the matter of the shrieking from the front yard.

Look, it's a beautiful gum tree, but I rented the house after it had finished blooming and fruiting, so was unaware of its demonic power. Over the following months, branch after branch put out round, woody fruits and bunches of fuzzy flowers, weighing the tree down and filling the air with a honeyed fragrance. How whimsical. How romantic. At least it would be, if it wasn't infested with shouting birds. Lorikeets, mainly. Hundreds of them. Every afternoon, from about 2pm until nightfall, the branches fill with these screeching, walloping, flapping maniacs. They go at the gum like vultures to a funeral pyre – tearing apart the fruit, squawking and squabbling, dropping leftovers on the footpath, driveway, lawn. Little, sticky, figgy, seed piles are everywhere. On the kids' shoes. On my shoes. Through the house.

And when twilight mercifully descends, and you feel as though peace is on the wind because the birds have finally fucked off into the blue evening? The bats arrive. Dear lord, the bats. They howl through the night.

But aside from the nightly shrieking, and The Shack's other ish-shews, being 'unmarried' isn't so bad. Every second weekend, I am all alone. By myself. In my empty house. People with children know that this is like finding a million dollars stashed under your floorboards, or inventing Facebook. For the first time in eleven years, I am absolutely free to spend my time as I choose. Like a teenager, or a cat.

I decide to take Bonnie's advice, and marry myself. Over the first few solo weekends, I develop a routine. I wake up at 6am on Saturday as my body clock is now set to toddler.

I take a strong cup of tea and a couple of shortbread biscuits out to the enclosed lattice-verandah, settle in on the couch, and drink slowly, dunking the bikkies. I scroll through every app on my phone. Marinate in the lives of others. Dive down Reddit rabbit holes and into Twitter feuds. Eat more biscuits. Do deep, stalky Facebook searches for boys I used to know, or people at work who look a bit interesting, or the day care mum whose kid bit Leo on the arse cheek. After a couple of hours of this debauchery, I get up and clean the house. Tidy and vacuum. Stack the dishwasher. Put the dirty clothes in the washing machine, and pour bleach down the drains and onto the shower floor tiles. Then, with all the appliances grinding away, I make another cup of hot tea and sit on my bed, turn on the small television my friend Alex gave me, and watch every show I've missed since 2005.

I stream entire seasons of *Gilmore Girls, Mad Men, Arrested Development* and *The West Wing*. I watch films, documentaries, stand-up comedy, sappy rom-coms, musicals. I get out of bed only to stand in front of the fridge and eat bits of cheese. I pluck oily sundried tomatoes from the jar and eat them with torn chunks of baguette. Sweet bread-and-butter pickles. Prosciutto. Chilli sardines. Food for grown-ups. In the afternoon, I go to the bakery and buy a steak and mushroom pie and a caramel tart, and once, a whole carrot cake with cream-cheese icing. I eat it with a fork in front of *The Notebook*, watching Ryan Gosling put his beautiful hand over his heart and shout, 'What do you want?' to an impossibly gorgeous Rachel McAdams, as crumbs fall down my chest.

I marry myself harder than I've ever been married before, and I am an exemplary wife. Loving, sassy, independent, brilliant. Gradually, parts of my soul return from wherever they had gone, like naughty little runaway boys coming home to Mummy, remorseful and chastened. Where have you been? It's intoxicating. I feel happier than I've ever felt before.

On Sunday arvos, I walk to the bowlo just up the road from The Shack. It's low-key sixties brick. Red carpet, Carlton Dry bunting, chalk boards. There's a small dance hall attached, and a 'ladies lounge' with couches, doilies and a picture of the queen on the wall. Behind the bar there is cheap beer, terrible wine, and pork crackling in plastic packets. Old men smoke and bowl. Old ladies wear visors and sip cans of Sprite. I know people here. Old neighbours, families from school, the couple who own the corner shop. I pull up a chair at a picnic table with Leisa, Sue, Nicole, Jo and Jen. An assortment of their kids flit about, playing tag and running on the green. Their husbands mill about the food truck and the bar, watching the footy on the TV.

The girls are planning a night out. Nicole is in charge because Nicole is good at being in charge and we are good at letting her being in charge. She has her phone out making bookings. Nicole and I are forever bonded. We both became unexpectedly pregnant with our third children at the same time. Borhan and I lived in a tiny, matchbox house on Laura Street, and Nic and her family lived across the road. We spent many an hour sitting together on the footpath, breastfeeding, while our other kids played. Neither of the babies slept. Both of them were nocturnal. We existed in a haze.

Things happened on Laura Street. One of Nic's daughters fell out of a leopard tree. Her fall was broken by my already tired and dinted Commodore, parked underneath. The plumbing of the matchbox house was a thousand years old and the landlord wouldn't replace it, so twice a year I found myself shovelling other people's shit out of the backyard. The babies ran off down the street together in Superman capes and nearly got run over by a bus. A snake slithered up into my car's engine. An owl flew into the house and perched on the end of William's bed. Borhan caught it in a blanket. Leo drank a cup of Pimm's at a backyard party. We lost the kids trick-or-treating, many times. Nicole used to say that house was haunted. They've bulldozed it now. Built a monument over it. Rendered, windowed-chic, glass and tile.

I sip my drink. Sue is talking to me. Asking about my writing. I tell her I'm not sure what to write about, where to head with it. I ask her what she would like to read. Sue is a smart woman, and good with a yarn. I trust her. 'I would love to read a story about your grandmother,' she says, sipping her pale ale. 'You should write about that.'

Later in the evening, Leisa and Nicole and I sit together behind the green. We light up a sneaky dart to share away from the kids. Leisa has bought a new house, right next door to the old one. Her four kids are teenagers now. They need more space.

'We're not going to sell number seventy-five . . .' Leisa says.

'Oh?' says Nicole.

'We're going to rent it out . . . to you.' She smiles at me.

'What?' I laugh.

A cheer goes up from the green. Alma has bowled a pearler.

'If you want it?'

It would be amazing to live in that house. Olive trees frame the front porch, there's a gas cooker, and the back deck is big enough to be a second lounge room.

'That is a very cool offer, Leis. I'd love to be your neighbour. But, I can't afford it. You'll get much more a week than what I could pay, with that sexy deck. Four rooms . . .'

'What do you pay now?' she asks.

I tell her how much rent I pay for the shrieking shack.

'That'll do us,' she says easily. 'We'd love to be neighbours with you. It's worth more than the extra cash.'

'Leis . . .' I'm touched. I start to tear up. Leisa isn't a woman who spends a lot of time crying. She nudges me with her shoulder. 'Just pack your stuff and come. It's done.'

'Don't you need to talk to Kris?' We look over at the boys. Barefoot bowling. Eating chicken wings. Ragging on each other about who sucks the most.

'We both love you, Seets. We're getting a great deal here too.'

Nicole nods in agreement. 'You're an awesome neighbour . . . and your car catches falling children.'

We laugh about the Bommodore, and clink our glasses.

I'm moving to Sunshine Avenue.

Ten months ago.

'I mean, maybe we could go back to mine?' he suggests.

'I didn't think that was an option.'

'Well, it's not ideal, no. It's bloody Piccadilly Circus during the day, but we might get away with it this time of night.'

'Will that be cool?'

He squints into the distance. 'I'm *pretty* sure Airbnb says you can have a guest?'

'But it would be poor form?'

The CityGlider squeals to a stop on Grey Street. A hen's party tumbles out.

'I'd love you to come back.'

Anthony lives in one room at a lodging house in Highgate Hill. He's rented the room while he's performing in the show. There are several other people living in the house, including the proprietors: Kevin, a gaunt computer technician and staunch anti-vaxxer who Anthony says could readily drop 'shaman' or 'age of aquarius' into conversation without irony; and his partner Kuntum, a floating West End socialite in a sarong.

The Uber is at the lodge in eight minutes. In that time, I consider my options. This is our fourth date and I'm actually going home with him. It's not a park. There's no bench on which to fumble about foolishly, like we have been doing for two weeks. No river view to keep us honest. No night-time strollers with small dogs. There's a bed. And a bathroom. And the definite possibility that we will lie down together in a small room between a farting FIFO miner and a young Chinese engineer, both of whom Anthony has a strained acquaintance with. Eight minutes is not long enough to chew on this.

On the vine-covered front porch, he signals for me to take off my shoes. I slip them off and hide them behind some others on the stoop. It's a gorgeous timber cottage – old workers' with high ceilings and beautifully carved architraves above the doors. We enter the lodge quietly and tiptoe down the hall past a tastefully furnished living room, bohemian cushions scattered artfully about, paintings adorning every spare space of the walls. Apart from the overwhelming presence of every-thing elephant, it's just the sort of place I love – clean but lived in, comfortable and warm. We sneak to his room, the middle of three, and he pushes the door open, silently.

There's something extraordinarily intimate about a single room.

Anthony flicks on the shaded bedside lamp and it casts a warm glow over his small corner of the world. There's a low, neatly made bed with a grey comforter, a wooden desk and chair in the corner, and an open wardrobe hugging the far wall. The wall is lined with wavy glass casement windows that open outwards to an enclosed verandah. There are four shirts hanging in the cupboard; under them, a small suitcase. Beside the bed is a cabinet – a tube of lip balm, Frank Herbert's *Dune*, and a reference book with papers sticking out of it. An empty red wine bottle is on the desk, along with a pile of DVDs and a neat stack of books. A little rattan hutch next to the door holds toiletries – floss, mouthwash, Lynx Voodoo body spray.

'Would you like a drink of water?'

'Yes, please.' I'm nervous and my mouth is papery.

He puts his satchel down on the desk chair and pads out of the room. I take my coat off and drape it over the chair, trying to make it look like I've tossed it casually, by laying it on a jaunty angle. I put my clutch on the desk and stand between the bed and the wardrobe, smoothing down my hair, wondering if I should sit down on the bed. I should. It will look weird if I stand and stare at the walls. I adjust my undies under my skirt and sit down demurely on the end of the bed. I read the spines of the books and plays on the desk – trying to remain present rather than catapult myself into a future that hasn't happened. A stack of high-brow tomes of the Western canon next to a teetering pile of Tarantino. I need to cough but I stifle it. I lean over and grab my clutch, rapidly apply a swathe of lipstick, and then wipe it all off with a tissue so it leaves a light stain. I stuff the tissue and lipstick back into my clutch and quickly sit down at an angle I hope looks relaxed, casually alluring.

He comes back with tap water in two potted mugs with elephant-trunk handles. I say mildly, 'Who did you play in *The Crucible?*'

He sits down next to me on the bed, handing me a mug.

'Hale one time, Proctor another. Sorry, these mugs are a bit hectic.'

We sip our waters. The lip of the mug is thick and water dribbles down my chin.

I gesture to the four shirts hanging in the cupboard, and wipe my face with the back of my hand in a manner that is neither casual, nor alluring.

'I love a man who lives light,' I say.

'Yep. No home. No car. No money. Four shirts. Form an orderly queue.'

I laugh quietly. 'I love that you live like this; I would love to live like this.'

'I feel pretty displaced, but it's cosy,' he says, lying down on the bed with a sigh of relief. It's midnight and he's done a matinee and an evening show. I put my mug on the bedside table and lie down next to him, on my side.

'I do have some more stuff, you know,' he says after a sheepish silence.

'I don't care about stuff,' I say, moving my hand onto his chest. He covers it with his.

I mean it. I don't care about things. I never have. If I feel my home getting too full of stuff, I cull mercilessly. My favourite week of the year is council collection week, when I merrily put my worldly goods out onto the footpath to be rummaged through by vagrants and drifters with utes and children on bikes. My kids regularly put post-it notes on things: 'Mum do not throw this away.' Often, I play a game with myself: supposing my house burnt down, what would I miss? What couldn't I live without? I adore my purple coat, but I could find another. I have a pair of cowboy boots that I wear all the time, but they're falling apart. I suppose it's the little mementos I would regret: a small cornflower-blue ceramic vase that used to belong to Fari; framed pieces of art the kids have produced over the years – chickens, houses, self-portraits; a watercolour of three trees that Jamal did for me.

When Dolly died, I asked my mother if I could have her one possession: a beautiful ruby necklace with a gold chain. The gemstone had an Arabic engraving on it – a mystical symbol made with winding golden strokes and little stars that meant 'God is the all Glorious'. She wore it every day, and I would have loved to have kept it. Fari told me that Dolly would be buried with it around her neck. I was upset but I didn't show it. I knew if I had said I wanted it when she was alive, my grandmother would have told me to take it and wear it, or take it and not wear it, but she would have pressed it onto me. If I had said I wanted the moon she would have pulled it out of the sky and put it in my palm. But Fari always said, about anything I wanted, 'You don't need it. You don't need anything. Be detached from the things of this world, Sita – it's made of dust.' Dramatic, but I suppose when you have lost the one thing that really matters, you have less patience for the world and everything in it. Fari would walk away from a blazing house without even a backward glance.

All we really have to keep in this world are moments. Our small lives are a strung necklace of them, each one catching the light at a different angle, casting different colours; some small and burnt like coal, some blue-blunt, some crisply rutted, and some round and fat and warm – like amber sap. A baby is born and a bead glows sunshine yellow, a teenager dies and tar infuses steel, carved metal against the skin.

The rain starts again, hitting the corrugated roof of the lodge in fits and starts. The wind is pulling up.

'What do you want?' he asks.

The first time I had sex was on my wedding night. I was twenty years old. According to Bahá'í law, 'sexual intercourse is permissible only between a man and the woman who is his wife'. Borhan and I had just turned twenty when we married. I loved the thought of being a wife. I loved referring to him as my husband. It felt so grown up. Sex was a fantastic and wonderful mystery to me. The next great frontier.

Now, twenty years later, in this bed in Highgate Hill, I think about all this. I think about God. I think about sex. I think about love. I think about moments. I think that outside these walls, the world is burning up with disease, raging with floods and pointless wars. Half the planet is locked down in their houses, or breathing through face masks in the streets, shops and parks. Afghanistan has been reclaimed by those murderous fanatics the Taliban; they're imposing Sharia law, stoning women in the streets, taking limbs in the name of Allah, the most Gracious, the most Merciful. Vladimir Putin has just invaded Ukraine. His army is shelling hospitals. Sick children and pregnant women are now dead under the hot rubble. And here in Brisbane, a town so unimportant and unobserved it is usually spared tragedy, our river has burst its banks. Houses are flooded, bridges are breaking and pontoons are floating away. Mother Nature is claiming the mud-caked debris of people's lives and showing us that even here in our sleepy city at the end of the earth, we cannot hide from catastrophe.

The God of all that is good is also the God of no good.

So, when the moment of truth arrives, and Anthony, flushed and brilliant-eyed and moving in the way men do when they have something in front of them that they cherish, suddenly holds himself quite still and asks, 'What do you want?'

. . . it's easy to find the answer.

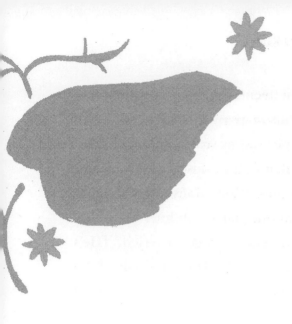

2016. Brisbane.

I'm packing my things into boxes and preparing to move to The Shack. I don't want to take anything other than my clothes and the kids' clothes and a few toys. I want to pack as though I'm going on a holiday, so I can pretend my divorce isn't really happening. Also, I don't want to put Borhan out. The only thing I really want is the Dyson vacuum. I asked if I could take it, but Borhan said he needed it to get rid of the cat hair. He's got me there. The cat is staying with Borhan, and Will is allergic.

I pull down the ladder to the attic and climb up. I hate the attic. I hate rodents. I poke my head through the manhole expecting to see a furry face with little red eyes in the corner, waiting to hurl itself at my jugular. Instead I see a box labelled 'Sita sentimental'.

The box is full of photos and knick-knacks from my school and university days. A bottle filled with origami stars that

Andy folded for me on my sixteenth birthday; a stuffed cow my friend Amanda (Moo) Millson gave me when I graduated; a yearbook signed by all the girls in my year. Virginia Howard had sticky-taped a condom into it with the inscription 'Cowboys do it better'. A mix CD from my friend James – Sheryl Crow, They Might Be Giants and Jamiroquai – with liner notes that said, 'If we don't find anyone else, let's get married.' (He's married now. Two kids. Rachel is lovely.) Down the side of the box is a little plastic photo album from Crazy Clarks, filled with pictures of my first year of university. And there is Mark, looking as gorgeous as the day I first saw him in the college car park, unloading his bags.

Mark Hayes was a curly-haired boy who studied musical theatre at my university but was heterosexual. Mark had a steady, blonde, pretty girlfriend called Quinn, who played the flute. Her hair was so thick and straight that if a small hurricane took it, it would fall back into place perfectly and survey the damage with insouciance. Mark and I were at college together, and Quinn was a year younger – still at school. He had a picture of her wearing a red top and looking winsome on the chest of drawers in his dorm room.

Mark and I paired up in tutorials. We walked to lectures together. He laughed at my jokes. He looked at me all the time. My late teens were spent reading novels by the Brontë sisters, watching Rodgers and Hammerstein musicals and bingeing soft American teen dramas. Except, you couldn't really binge in the nineties, you had to record that week's episode on VHS and re-watch the same one until the following week. This led me to at least fifty memorised episodes of *Dawson's Creek*, and some absurdly unrealistic notions of romance, men and sex. But at least I knew when a boy was looking at me.

Once, I pretended to fall asleep on the floor of the dorm common room after a midnight movie, to see what he would do. Mark carried me back to my bed. When he picked me up I put my face against his neck. He smelled like Herbal Essences shampoo, Rexona for Men, and the spaghetti bolognaise from the college dining hall. He was perfect. I knew that him and Quinn had lost their virginity to one another. I knew that he loved her. But I knew that he wanted me too.

One night after a party, our friend Chase was passed out between us on the couch. Chase was also in love with Mark. He had even less chance with him than me, so he'd chosen to drink his way through it and lean heavily into wearing singlets with terry-towelling shorts. His head was on my lap, and his bare legs on Mark. We were watching 2am telly. Mark put his hand out, palm up, over Chase's back, and looked at me. I took it and we held hands and fell asleep. Well, he fell asleep. I lay there feeling his palm on mine and wondering how my hand felt to him, willing it to feel as soft and delicate and enchanting as possible so that he would fall in love with me. A week later, Quinn came to stay in the dorm for a few nights. They only emerged for meals.

That winter I met Borhan at a Bahá'í youth camp in Boonah. We were nineteen. Borhan was smart and tall, and had a quiet intensity that I found compelling. He was giving lectures at the camp. He gave a lecture called 'Feminism and the Bahá'í Faith' that I thought was the most original and thought-provoking thing I had ever heard. At nineteen, it probably was. Men weren't feminists in 2001. In their most radical moments they supported feminists, but they were never the ones carrying the placards. Iranian-Australian men were definitely not feminists. A couple of years later, after we were married, I laughed when he brought home a whole raw chicken for me to make a curry. I told him, 'I don't touch raw chicken. It makes me feel sick.' He told me I needed to get over it. That we couldn't build a life together if I couldn't touch chicken. That I was being childish. I remember thinking, as I held the goosebumpy pink leg and puckered torso skin and tried to hack through it with a knife, that he couldn't really be a feminist if he wanted me to touch this slippery shit.

I always thought I was the type of person who couldn't hold a grudge. Andy complains that I never remember any of my fights with men and it makes me too forgiving. I pride myself on this. It makes me feel benevolent and evolved to take the high road and forgive those who've wronged me. Also, I think it's the right thing to do. But when Borhan and I split, fifteen years later, I vowed I would go to my grave without ever touching another piece of raw chicken. That's how you build a divorce. One little resentment at a time.

When I met Borhan in Boonah he was almost uncomfortably polite, an old man in a young body, and as earnest about his faith in God as any zealot in Christendom. I think subconsciously I found this appealing because my father was such an advocate, and aren't girls supposed to marry their fathers? I also liked the fact that he was talked about. He was the new rising star of the Bahá'í faith. He was an academic too, and the type of scholar who had such a terrific memory he could tell you the date each Prophet was martyred, not only on the Gregorian calendar, but also the Badí' calendar.

We lived in different cities, so our courtship was mainly by email. This was before smartphones. His emails were so clever, sometimes witty, but always erudite. I pursued him, and when I knew he liked me, I backed off and let him chase me. Nobody taught me that was how to get a husband. I just knew. And I didn't have any experience to make me cynical or insecure.

I'm sure I hurt him brutally over the years, but no worse than the first time he told me he loved me, when I said . . . 'I love you too, but not as much as I love Mark Hayes.'

I had a psychologist tell me once that we choose people who wound us in the way our mothers and fathers wounded us. We enjoy the cuts they give us because it makes us feel secure. It makes us feel the nurturing embrace of childhood, even if our childhood was grotesque and dysfunctional. I wonder what happened to me in my early years that made me feel it was okay to tell someone who had just said 'I love you' that I loved someone else more; that they were, at this stage of the race, coming second.

I was just being honest with Borhan. I thought that's what being in a relationship was all about. I had Fari's voice in my ear saying: 'Truthfulness is the foundation of all human virtues,' and 'Even if a lie is as small as a grain of rice, you shouldn't tell it.' I should have known which lies wouldn't stick in my throat. I now know that honesty is not what a relationship is about. A relationship is about apologising.

I pulled my phone out of my back pocket and sat down on the dusty floor of the attic. I searched for Mark Hayes on Facebook. I wondered if he was still with Quinn, or if they were divorced. I wondered if he was still handsome. I fantasised that he was single and that I would send him a message and he would say he had been thinking about me on and off for years. But I couldn't find him anywhere online. He had disappeared. And so had I.

2017. Brisbane.

'So why does Clarissa choose to marry boring, self-contained Richard Dalloway, and not the sexy and passionate Peter Walsh?' I ask the class.

It's term four. We are studying *Mrs Dalloway* by Virginia Woolf. The kids hate it.

'Because Peter's a simp!' calls out Josh. It's thirty-seven degrees in Brisbane today and he's standing up near the open glass doors of the low-ceiling classroom, fanning himself with his brand new, unthumbed copy of the novel. One hand in his shorts pocket.

'Yeah, Miss, nobody likes a needy guy. He's just doing everything she wants so she'll like him, but that's a turn-off for her,' says Zoe.

'She's not turned off, ay,' says Malik. 'Duh. She's gay. She's in love with that Sally chick.'

'No, she isn't. Nothing happens with Sally,' says Harvinder, a chubby boy with white teeth and an A+ average. 'She's marrying the boring man for his money.'

'It's the nineteen-twenties, Harv. She can't just come out,' says Erin, chewing gum with her mouth open.

'What d'you reckon, Miss?' asks Malik.

My mind has wandered. I'm staring blankly at the front row. It's been happening lately.

'Miss?' he repeats.

'Hm? Sorry . . .' I say, wiping away the drop of sweat that is threatening to trickle down the side of my face, with my wrist.

'You were telling us why she married Richard and not Peter,' says Katie, in a soft voice.

'She doesn't want to disappear,' I say. 'She's marrying boring Richard because she wants to keep her independence. She wants to keep the inner workings of her soul private.'

Blank stares. I press on.

'In so many ways, Clarissa Dalloway mirrors Virginia Woolf herself. Remember this?' I point to a print-out on the wall.

'"I need solitude. I need space. I need air. I need the empty fields round me; and my legs pounding along roads; and sleep; and animal existence."'

I point to another, 'Or this one from *The Waves*.

'"How much better is silence; the coffee cup, the table. How much better to sit by myself like the solitary sea-bird that opens its wings on the stake. Let me sit here for ever with bare things, this coffee cup, this knife, this fork, things in themselves, myself being myself."'

Virginia Woolf was basically every mother with three kids and a mortgage in the 'burbs, who just wanted some fucking space to breathe. Only she had no kids and no mortgage. She had a bohemian split-level in London, a tranquil weatherboard cottage in Sussex, and a wonderful, doting husband called Leonard who published her novels and spent every day looking after her and hoping she wouldn't kill herself. Which she did anyway.

'Peter loves Clarissa, right? Wildly. But he wants love and obsession. She knows that will be wonderful for a little while, but eventually it will trap her. If she marries Peter, she will think of him all the time – he'll make sure of it. They'll be consumed by what each other is feeling and doing. And she will give everything she has to fill the massive hole inside him which can never really be filled, because Peter is a hungry ghost.'

'What's a hungry ghost?' asks Zoe, captivated. Josh has wandered off to the toilets. Harvinder is scratching notes.

'It's a Buddhist idea, but there are Hindu hungry ghosts as well,' I explain. 'They're tormented souls with enormous bellies as huge as mountains. The problem is they have skinny little necks like straws and mouths as small as the hole of a needle. So, they're doomed to wander the earth hungry and thirsty forever. Never able to be satisfied.'

'Like you, bro.' Malik ribs Harv. The class giggles.

'Don't fat shame me until you can read,' he responds to applause.

'The hungry ghost is a metaphor for desire.' I lift my voice to shut down the hubbub. 'Hungry ghosts are people who are always wanting. Never satisfied or content with what they have. Like Peter Walsh. Even though Clarissa loves Peter, rather than face a life trying to satisfy him, she marries someone stable. Well-mannered. Aloof. I mean Richard's no great, passionate lover. But, he's happy with what he has. He doesn't want more from her all the time. And that gives her freedom.'

Silence. Glazed eyes. Red cheeks.

'And yeah, look. She's probably gay.' The room erupts in laughter as the bell rings for lunch.

'Hit save and shut down your laptops please,' I call over the clatter. 'We'll start our first body paragraphs next lesson.' The room is filled with the sound of keyboards clacking, bags zipping, scraping chairs, chatter. 'Erin, spit that gum out into the bin on your way out.' I head back to my desk to pack up. The room clears. I flop down in my chair and rub my sweaty eyes. I cannot wait to get to the air-conditioned staff room for forty-five minutes of sweet relief.

'Miss . . .' murmurs Katie Jeanes. She's materialised right next to me. Shock of curly blonde hair falling over her right shoulder. Almond eyes. Perfect sprinkle of freckles across the bridge of her nose. Smart. Polite. Frustratingly shy. The type of person who could rule the world if she would only open her mouth.

'Hey Katie, you okay?' I ask, thinking of sausage rolls and chocolate Breakas from the tuck-shop.

'I . . . I was just wondering . . .' she stalls. There is literally no breeze in this room. I feel faint.

'Go ahead, honey . . .' I prompt.

'I was just wondering if you were okay. Actually,' she says like a mouse, looking at my desk.

'Me?' I reply with genuine surprise. 'Why do you ask?'

'You just seem a bit different lately, Miss. Like, still funny and everything. But, a bit sad. I think you're a great teacher and I thought I should ask you if you were okay.' She pushes the last part out of her mouth uneasily. Her face blushes.

I take a deep breath in and feel myself unexpectedly welling up. Malik bursts back into the room. 'Forgot my friggin' hat,' he blurts. Then he sees my face.

'What's wrong, Miss?' he scoops up his hat and approaches my desk.

'Katie was just asking me the same thing,' I said.

'Yeah, you've been a bit suss lately, ay Miss. We been keepin' an eye on ya.'

Katie looks supremely uncomfortable that this conversation now has another participant. The fan ticks slowly. The room is a touch cooler without the twenty-five extra bodies. I decide to level with the pair of them.

'I might be a bit off because I've split up from my husband,' I say flatly.

'Naaaaah way . . .' Malik breathes out earnestly, 'Miss . . . that's dog.'

Katie gives gentle nods.

'I'm okay. It happens. I'm just worried about my kids,' I say, wondering why I'm saying it. I suppose it's because they asked. Sometimes teenagers can envelop you with such generous openness that you become a bit more of what you were then, and a bit less of what you've become now.

'Your kids will be ace, Miss!' says Malik like a hype guy at a sports concert. 'My parents split up and it was a big deal because they're Muslim and shit, but honestly, it was the best for my bro and me. We became so close. You're cool, Miss. With a mum like you, they're gonna be so good.'

My heart swells for this strutty boy who just last week was suspended for putting Tyler Beauchamp into a skip bin and padlocking it shut. (In his defence, Tyler is very annoying. Malik was only doing what many of us have fantasised about doing for years. Ken Hudson, Tyler's maths-in-society teacher, called it 'community service' because while Tyler was in the skip he missed period four.)

I smile. 'Thanks, Malik. That's very kind of you. And I do appreciate the vote of confidence.'

'I gotchu, Miss,' he says solemnly, puffing out his scrawny chest like a Samoan nightclub bouncer. It's so endearing I almost want to hug him.

'Last year my dad realised he was gay and left my mum for a horse trainer named Les,' says Katie.

Malik's eyes widen. I clear my throat.

'Yeah. It was pretty, um, weird,' she whispers, brushing her hair out of her eyes. She looks at Malik. 'Don't tell anyone.'

He shakes his head. 'Nah, we cool, Katie. That's shit though, ay.'

'That's a lot to deal with, honey. I'm sorry you've had to,' is what I can think of to say.

'My cousin reckons she's a lesbian . . .' says Malik, opening a packet of salt and vinegar chips from his bag. 'But you can't be a Muslim and a lesbian. Well, you can. But you can't say that you are.' He crunches into a fistful of chips meaningfully.

'Is your mum all right?' I ask Katie.

'Yeah, she's all right,' she says. 'I think she probably knew, but I don't really ask her about it. I love my dad. And my mum. But it's their stuff, not mine. If your kids know that this is your stuff, not theirs, they'll be okay, Miss.'

I spent the rest of the day wondering if the kids knew it was our stuff and not theirs. I'd been watching them over the last months. Catching them in pensive moments and wondering if they were thinking about the split.

We took the kids to the Salisbury McDonald's on a Sunday morning to tell them we were separating. We wanted to pick somewhere neutral. Somewhere they wouldn't have to visit frequently and be reminded of an awful and possibly traumatising chat. We didn't even use the words 'divorce' or 'separation'. They seemed too violent. Red chillies for our babies to swallow. Instead we told them we were married now, but we weren't going to be married anymore – we were getting 'unmarried'. How absurd. How utterly ridiculous. My mouth was like Styrofoam. The smell of cheeseburger meat was making me nauseous. Layla, our eldest, was ten years old. She didn't say anything. She sat completely still and breathed slowly through her nose, until tears began falling down her cheeks. Leo, only three, banged his little fist on the table happily. He knocked over the orange juice. 'Uh oh!' he giggled as the tacky juice spilled into the tray. His chips floated in it.

Rescuing his nuggets and sauce from the slop, William said, 'Will there be a party?'

'What, sweetie?' I murmured, rubbing Layla's back.

'A party with cake? Like when you get married you get a cake. Do you get a cake when you get un-married?' he asked with no trace of irony.

'No buddy, there's no party. But we can get a cake if you like?' Borhan replied, optimistically.

I was too horrified to speak.

1996. Toowoomba.

'Which one is coming for sleep tonight?' calls Dolly from her recliner.

'Carly, Grans,' I say with my head deep in the refrigerator, looking for last night's leftover apple crumble.

It's the fourth of November. My fifteenth birthday. Fari never lets me go to sleepover parties. My eldest sister went to one in 1983 and the kids watched *Creepshow* on VHS. Lisa was so terrified she broke out in hives. Since then none of us have been allowed to sleep anywhere but in our own beds. But I'm allowed to have whoever I want come stay at Bridge Street.

'Which one is Carly? The fat one? Or the one with the things on her teeths?' Dolly asks.

'Penny is the one with braces.' I say, spooning cold apple crumble out of the foil tin and into my mouth. 'Carly isn't fat. You can't say fat . . . but you're thinking of Sarah.'

'Yes, that Sarah is fat. These Australie girls . . . all fat.' she muses, opening a *Women's Weekly*.

'Grans!' I object.

'If you were Australie, you be fat too,' she shrugs, licking her thumb and turning the page.

My brother is buttering toast in the kitchen. 'You can't call people fat, Grans. You have to say "big-boned" or "plea-sant-ly plum-p".'

'Okay . . .' she says obediently. 'That Sarah is a plea-sant plump.'

'Much better!' he praises, pulling himself up to sit on the kitchen bench, half a slice of Vegemite toast hanging from his mouth. 'Now say: "Jamal has mas-sive mus-cles".'

'Ja-mal is a di-ck he-ad,' I enunciate, taking the bottle of milk out of his hand to finish making my tea.

'Carly is the crazy one, right Seets?' he asks.

'Oh, crazy Carly. She is good.' Dolly nods, reaching out for her coffee with a shaky hand. Jamal jumps off the bench and slides it closer to her. He fixes her brown crocheted knee-rug as well, tucking it into the sides of the recliner. She pats his cheek.

'She is not crazy,' I say. 'She's just . . . excited about things. And you can't call people crazy, either.'

Carly has attention deficit hyperactivity disorder. She's on Ritalin. I am devoted to her. She's hilarious. She says what she thinks and she dances and sings and plays games – even though we are in year ten at school and not technically supposed to play anymore. She is the least boring girl I know.

Tonight, we're dressing up and watching *Tank Girl*. We'll make our own pizzas and eat a whole Viennetta log and say all the lines along with Lori Petty and Naomi Watts. Obviously, Carly is Tank Girl (badass fem-anarchist with a massive army tank between her legs. Saving the future. Punching blokes in the balls). And I'm Jet Girl (nerdy but brilliant engineer turned badass fem-anarchist in jet goggles. Saving the future. Punching blokes in the balls).

I put Dolly to bed before the movie starts. I put her to bed most nights. I don't remember when it began, because we've always been like this. An unspoken care arrangement that was written in the book of fate as soon as John put me in her arms fifteen years ago. I shower her and towel her off. I brush her wet hair – a short black and grey bob. I dab Johnson & Johnson's talcum powder under her arms and in the soft folds of her elbows and knees and neck. I pull her knee-length culottes on and lift her arms through her night-shirt. I walk her to her room, arm in arm, help ease her down to a seated position on her bed, and pull her arthritic legs up when she lays down. Then I tuck her in, push her hair back out of her face, kiss her cheek, and we say a prayer together before she sleeps. Sometimes I lie down beside her to watch something on her tiny, wall-mounted telly. *Family Ties* or *Full House*, or maybe an episode of *Neighbours* if she's having an early night.

Tonight, though, I want to be with my friend watching *Tank Girl*. I rush the powder and brush her hair with rough strokes. I tap impatiently on her wet foot to get her to lift it into her pants, trot her to bed, and speed through the shortest prayer I know.

The movie finishes. The house is still. The windows of the family room are open. The smell of night beetles and jasmine floats in on a cool breeze. The cicada buzz has died down. Fari is in bed, nodding off. The desk light is on in John's study. He's balancing a tax return, humming athletically to Rachmaninoff's third piano concerto. Jamal is at his mate Stuey's house, watching the soccer. Carly and I have eaten all the pizza and all the ice-cream and an enormous pile of Samboy barbecue chips and a bowlful of Skittles. I feel sick. My mouth is furry. Carly rubs her eyes.

'Seets, can I have a towel?'

'Sure,' I say, yawning.

I toss Carly a towel from our messy linen cupboard and she heads to the bathroom.

We have one bathroom at Bridge Street. It has a large shower over a bath, with frosted glass sliding doors that lend a hint of privacy in what is the least private bathroom in the world. The lock has been broken since 1992 when Jamal fell into the door in an attempt to classic-catch a cricket ball my cousin Vinny chucked at him from the family room. Someone is always coming in to use the toilet, or brush their teeth, or do their hair, or tell you to hurry up and get out of the shower because you're using all the hot water. The bathmat is always wet. The handtowel is someone's forgotten bath towel. There's a little cardboard pyramid of spent toilet rolls next to the loo, two or three trashy magazines, a *Weekend Australian,* and a dog-eared Penguin Classics edition of *The Consolation of Philosophy* by Boethius. A pad of hand soap floats in an olive-green saucer next to a cupful of mismatched, fuzzy toothbrushes. The toothpaste tube, squeezed from the middle, has a gummy lid. It's touching the cord of my sister's baby-pink hairdryer. The hairdryer is plugged in and dangling from the towel ring. You can see all the way to the cubby-house through the basin window.

I hear Carly turn on the shower. I head to Dolly's room to check on her and kiss her goodnight. She is sitting up in bed.

'I need go toilet.'

Without thinking, I help her up and we make our way to the bathroom. Shit. Carly is showering. I'd forgotten.

'Grans, Carly is in the shower. Can you wait a little bit?' I ask as we stand outside the bathroom door.

'No waiting,' she says, twisting the handle.

Steam washes out into the hallway with the smell of coconut shampoo and soap. Carly has the frosted shower doors shut.

'Carls . . . so sorry,' I call through the door crack. 'My grandma needs to use the toilet.'

Grans is already shuffling towards the loo.

'That's all right!' Carly says.

I help Dolly down onto the toilet seat. She waves me away. 'I call you,' she says.

I shut the door behind me and wait nervously in the hall.

Dolly sits and waits. Relieving herself is not as easy as it used to be. Sometimes she feels like she can't wait to empty herself, but once she sits down, nothing comes. No matter. She has learnt to hold hands with the present moment. She picks up a magazine and thumbs through it.

Carly starts singing in the shower, belting out Alanis Morissette's 'Ironic'.

Dolly finishes and looks for the plastic one litre milk bottle to wash herself. It's missing. She knocks on the glass of the shower. Carly sticks her head out.

'Crazy Carly, give me cloth,' Dolly says smiling up at her.

'Cloth. Cloth. Cloth,' says Carly, looking around the shower. There's a pink face washer hanging over the stall door. She pulls it down and reaches around the shower door to hand it to Dolly.

'No. Wet it.'

Carly wets the washer and passes it through. Dolly uses the washer to clean herself. Then she reaches around and throws it back into the shower.

I hear Carly scream and I race back into the bathroom. Grans is attempting to stand up. Carly is laughing and squealing her head off. The shower door is wide open. She's huddled in the corner, as far away from the soiled face-washer as she possibly can be.

'Grans!' I squawk in horror. 'Oh my god!'

Dolly is ignoring the commotion and concentrating. She's holding the toilet-paper holder and reaching to pull up her culottes with her shaky free hand. She can't quite reach them. I bend over and yank them up, flush the toilet, pull her roughly to the basin and smack the soap at her hands, washing it off in splashes.

'I'm so sorry, Carls. I'll clean it up.'

My face is red. I'm embarrassed all the way down to my toenails. I'm shaking with it. Carly has turned off the shower and is unashamedly drying herself in plain view.

'It's okay!' she says from under the towel, buffing dry her short, platinum blonde hair. 'I just didn't expect a flying poo-washer.' She bursts out laughing again.

Not bothering with the handtowel, I link my elbow with Dolly's and fast-shuffle her back to her room. Carly is still cackling. 'It's all good, Grandma. Don't worry!' She calls out. Everybody called Dolly 'Grandma'. I steer her down the hall. We get to the bedroom and I'm steaming. How could she embarrass me like this? What if Carly tells people at school? I'm already the kid whose parents don't drink and are always talking about God, who isn't allowed to go to sleepovers, whose grandma calls the cafe and the movie theatre to see where she is. It's enough.

I lie Dolly down in her bed, chuck her feet up onto the mattress and whip the covers over her. I smack an angry kiss on her cheek and storm out of her room.

'Sita!' she calls. 'Sita!'

I ignore her and keep on walking.

'Sita!' she shouts.

I stop. I hammer my forehead with a balled fist. I storm back and yell: 'WHAT?'

'Nothing, Baba, nothing,' she says, quietly. Chastened.

I stalk off.

Carly and I go to bed. Carls is giggling and joking about the 'poo-washer'. I play along. Pretend it's all a laugh. Old people! How funny are they? She's on a mattress on the floor, and I'm in my bed. I turn the light off and say goodnight. I sit up and pretend I'm stretching out my back, but really, I'm saying my night-time prayers. I can't sleep unless I say them, and I can't disrespect God or his Prophets by saying them lying down. I'm quick about it.

In the morning my eyes open with a start. Carly is sleeping with her mouth agape, covers askew, legs hanging off the mattress. I replay last night's disaster over in my mind. I jump up softly and tiptoe to Dolly's room. What if she died during the night and the last thing I did to her was rough shoving and shouting? What if the last thing I said to her was mean? I would never forgive myself.

She's not dead. She's leaning up on two pillows watching a replay of the cricket. I flop down next to her and bury my head in her soft chest.

'I'm sorry,' I say, my face muffled.

She pats my back.

'You are my sunshine.'

'I was mean to you.'

'Is okay. You want a lolly?'

She reaches over to a jar on her nightstand and pulls out a gold-wrapped chocolate eclair.

'Sometimes I get angry at us, because I want to be like everyone else.'

She unwraps the eclair and puts it in my mouth.

'My Sita. You will never, ever, ever be like everyone else. But, one day your eyes will come open and you will see . . .' She opens her eyes wide and looks down at me, cupping my cheek with her hand.

'See what?' I ask.

'How you lucky, lucky, lucky girl.'

'Why am I lucky?' I ask, chewing into the sticky caramel.

'You lucky because you have one leg in this place and one leg in another. One brown leg and one white. You are magic. Two in one!'

'I don't want to be two in one. I want to be one in one.'

'Now you want be one. But later, you will see how two in one is better.'

'How?'

She unwraps another eclair and pops it into her cheek, gumming it toothlessly.

'You know both sides of this world. You know East and you know West. And the more you know, the better you live. Wherever you go, you not be scared. You not be fright. You can love instead.'

2019. Hluboká.

'Unnecessary crying,' Irie rasped in a husk of a voice.

Her mouth was slack. The cancer had contorted her lower lip and jaw. What was once a pleasantly plump body was now reedy and pale. She lay in her single bed, in a rose-covered nightie and a pair of woollen socks. Irie's grandchildren had arrived from Glasgow, and Haifa, and Berlin.

'There is no point in you all coming here if you are just going to cry.'

The doctor had told them it wouldn't be long.

'My ladies . . .' she said slowly to her eldest grandson, Jordan. 'My ladies are coming this week. I want them to have something nice.'

'Grandma, you can't take your class. You can't cook. You can't get out of bed. They will understand.'

'Jordan, my beta, I'm not dead yet.'

He took her thin hand between his two. 'Grandma, you're supposed to rest.'

'Rajah. Your granddaddy always used to say, "There are bold pilots, and there are old pilots, but there are no old-bold pilots." Now that I am old I have nothing left to lose. I want to be of service. My ladies are coming.'

She went on to give very specific catering instructions. Her grandchildren were to go to the only Indian restaurant in town and order ten curries, but not rice since the rice at the restaurant was 'hopeless'. They would cook fresh rice themselves. They would also make three salads, a raita, and fifty small pappadums – deep-fried, not roasted – for her guests. Then, they would set out the best crockery and cutlery, with matching crystal glasses, and they would converse in perfect English with her ladies for two hours, while serving them dinner.

As usual, Irie got exactly what Irie wanted. The ladies came. The ladies ate. The ladies left. Irie stayed in bed. Over the next week, friends and neighbours came to kiss her cheeks and bring gifts. Apples. Roses in pots. Fresh bread. A bottle of home-brewed rose vodka she was too polite to say she would never drink.

Moments were coming to her in flashes.

Phat-phat-phat! Satto. He's flying his chopper over their house in Jorhat. Thank God he is alive. Smack! The army doctor slaps her bare bottom with his palm. 'Stop screaming Mrs Williams. You're hysterical.' But the baby is coming. It hurts, it hurts. 'Kito'. We'll call him 'Kito'. The doorbell. Fawning visitors. Satt-Satt has done it. He's flown over the Himalayas with the governor, to drop the ashes of Prime Minister Nehru on the snowy mountains. Brown skates. Khodi laces them onto her feet. Her brother is holding her arm to steady her. 'Mona will never know,' he whispers. Dolly, pushing bread into her pocket. Mehri, putting rollers in her hair. Rambutans, green guava and fat mangoes. The fruit and vegetable markets in Suva. Where is Fari? She's not here. Shivani Khanum will be looking for her. The beach at Redcliffe is windy. Irie pushes Satto in his wheelchair along the shore of Moreton Bay. Goodbye my sweetie. We will meet again. A doll's house and trinkets. She kisses a baby with black curls. Is it Priya? Nikita, perhaps. Her baby boy, he's getting married. She's dancing in a red and gold sari, with bells on her ankles and white jasmine in her hair.

Dying was the least glamorous thing Irie would ever do. But she did it. And the world she loved so much, the sparkling, chain-of-hearts, star-anise world she made for herself and for us, is all the poorer for it.

2020. Brisbane.

The signing of my divorce papers has inspired a guilt renaissance. Thoughts and moments, chunks of the past are being dragged up like bodies out of a bog. Facing them or working through them or nutting out what happened and why would be difficult and painful, which is why I've chosen to address my feelings with a cleaning bender. The type where skirting boards are involved. Marie Kondo would rejoice. Does this shelving unit that usefully holds every craft supply we own spark joy? No. To the pavement it goes! Does the florid pattern on this melamine crockery make me feel irrelevant? Yes! Out it goes. The bookshelves are molested by dust. The cushion covers look haggard. The bathroom tiles are gangrenous. I'm affronted by my rugs. I'm eating a family-sized pack of Maltesers without even sucking on them. Just crunching through malted spheres one after another so they stick to my molars.

Here's the thing about Borhan: he does completely mad things. He quit his job at a top-tier law firm to start his own international leasing business with no capital. He went to

Vietnam to have all his suits tailor-made. He had twenty tonnes of soil delivered to his suburban front yard to make a sustainable vegetable plot in his backyard. Didn't plant a bean. He went to Bali to meet a Shaman who would guide him through ceremonial cleansing rituals on Skull Island (aptly named for its abundance of human skulls – remnants of original Balinese open-air burial traditions). He was accused of witch-doctoring and chased through the Papua New Guinean jungle by deadly tribes. He slit a goat's throat to feed starving Romanian villagers. He was a child actor from Townsville who was expelled from school for kung-fu fighting in the playground. He threw a violin into the Ross River and watched it sink. He almost died from malaria. Twice. He bought the kids chickens and then when Will's chick Lucky (ironically) died, he curated a chicken funeral complete with floral tributes, speeches and glasses of aged scotch. He's pro-choice and abhors health mandates so he has plans to sell his house in the city two blocks from mine. He dreams of buying a plot of land in western Queensland and kitting out a home with solar panels so that he can live in an off-grid man-palace, shooting feral pigs, raising stock and increasing the world's bee population.

So, I'm cleaning.

I lug the lounge-room rug outside like a Dickensian urchin, hang it over the back deck and start beating it. The birds rise up out of the poinciana tree in one breath. The children flee to their rooms to avoid conscription. I wash the sheets, pillow cases, doona covers and tea towels and hang them on the clothesline. They flap in the sun like crooked teeth. I turn the radio up.

The Cranberries are playing 'Zombie'. I remove the head of the vacuum and use the hose and pipe to aggressively eliminate crumbs, broken bits of pasta, and other kitchen scurf lurking in drawers and corners. The house smells like musty vacuum fumes and bleach. I love bleach – it's one of the few things in life that can be counted on. I yank the toilet brush from its watery cylinder and enthusiastically squirt pine-scented cleaner into the toilet bowl.

Kafka writes about catching sight of things through 'gently shifting gaps in the foliage'. This is what it feels like to look back on my marriage and divorce. Through the hedged fence of separation, I can never really see the full picture.

The issue I have (I ponder, teeth gritted, eyes narrowed, scrubbing arm extended) is that the mad things Borhan does often seem to work out for the best. He inspires stress that I am sure has taken years off my life. But in the end, everything turns out all right. This is infinitely more irritating than the mad things themselves. There is no one alive who wants to be grateful to someone for divorcing them, or for challenging the foundations of their faith. But I am. You're supposed to hate the man you divorce. But I don't. It's very confusing. Concerning, actually. What kind of a monster forces her children into a gypsy-like existence to divorce someone she doesn't even hate?

I dip and scrub and splosh. Churning. I break a small sweat. One of the kids is standing behind me. 'What is it?' I ask, turning my head and expecting to hear a request to drive them immediately to the house of a friend with a sane mother. But nobody is there.

I drop the brush in the toilet and turn around. My eyes tell me that nobody is in the bathroom. But, overwhelmingly, my sixth sense tells me somebody is in the bathroom. I can't see them, but I feel them standing there. I know who it is.

'Aunty Irie?' I say quietly. 'Is that you?'

I move slowly to shut the bathroom door, as if that will stop the dead from escaping. I stand still and wait, my mind a blank, my senses on high alert. I don't believe in ghosts, or visitations, or witchcraft, or seances and summoning, or mediums. I don't believe in guardian angels, or devils, or bad luck or good luck, but I close my eyes.

'Aunty, are you here?'

Like a summer day, the room fills with beauty and warmth and love. I feel her embrace me. Her cheek is on my cheek. There is no night-time and there is no daytime. Tears begin to fall down my face as she holds me.

She says, 'You worry too much, Sita my darling. Don't worry. Be happy.' She laughs at her own joke. And then, in this timeless, placeless, formless world, she starts singing Bobby McFerrin. The absurdity of this makes me laugh aloud and squeeze my eyes even tighter shut. And all that there is in the universe is love and light and garnet leaves and grapes and kulfi and sunshine and sparkling jewels and dressing up and spiced lamb curry.

And then – just like it began – it's over. I open my eyes and stare at myself in the mirror of the empty bathroom, wiping my cheeks dry. She's gone. And so is my urge to clean.

2020. Cairns.

Cairns air sticks like glue. I've come here, to the sweaty armpit of the Daintree, to see my Aunty Mona. Outside the terminal, passengers from down south begin peeling off layers of clothing, stuffing cardigans and jackets into their carry-on luggage and looking through the heat with squinted eyes. In an instant it becomes acceptable to be bra-less in public. The thick-trunked king ferns, palms and jade creepers of Mount Whitfield cascade down to the tarmac on my left. Sea winds push sultry air towards me on the right. The north is so beautiful. It's a paradise. Which is why it's a shame that any sense of lusty romance this setting might evoke is put to death by the stupidly oppressive heat.

I'm under strict instructions from Fari not to catch a cab to Mona's house, but to wait at the airport for my cousin Nabil to pick me up. He's late. Nabil has recently finished his third bout of chemotherapy and I'm feeling guilty for asking him for a lift. But Fari insisted. Mona insisted. I lean lazily on the handle of my bag, a spritz of sweat forming on my upper lip, and wonder how people live in this soup.

I'm the last passenger in the pick-up zone when Nabil's white Toyota Yaris rattles up to the kerb. Wiping the sweat from his balding head – tufts of grey sprouting – he beams at me through the open passenger window and drawls, 'Hey cuz. Wanna lift?'

The Yaris contentedly pumps out hot air as we drive past the low-set bungalows and eighties brick and fibro homes, scattered palm trees, green and lush, gardens bursting out everywhere.

'I'm only staying three nights,' I say. 'Will there be room at your mum's? I'm happy to book a motel if I need to.'

'There's always room. People in and out. Don't worry, her house is a motel.'

Nabil zips into Mona's driveway and his car seizes with a wheeze. I look through the grubby windscreen and see that we've pulled up in front of a large, padlocked metal grate enclosing an airy carport. A large tatami mat lays on the concrete floor, chairs scattered round, the surrounding shelves of the little garage stuffed with kids' toys, pots, old suitcases, a stroller. A bright yellow sign hangs on the grate:

WARNING: Premises under 24-hr surveillance.

The house itself is modest, a low-set brick and tile affair, fighting to hold its own among banana trees, flamingo-coloured hibiscus bushes, agave shrubs and climbing weeds. An enormous orange and purple bird of paradise bush covers half the frontage of the house and soars above the windows, attempting to swallow the roof. The long, tiled porch is littered with pots, shoes, and low-slung canvas chairs in faded tropical colours. Nabil disappears into the leafy fray with my bag and I follow. I'm dying to change out of my jeans.

He knocks and calls, 'Ma, it's us.' There's a bustle and a rattle from the other side of the front door as the three metal latches clack open one by one. On the dusty front window screens, another yellow sign:

WARNING: CCTV cameras in operation.

Aunty Mona is the kind of woman other women wonder about in their quiet, suburban moments. I often think of her when I'm considering little things, like whether the thongs and pyjama pants I'm wearing to school pick-up look carefree or just cheap, or if I should send my coffee back because the barista put in two shots when I asked for one, or if my bathroom tiles need to be professionally cleaned before I host Christmas lunch and everybody sees how I actually live. Mona would never waste a minute on this stuff. She's a woman whose priorities have always been clear. She's not scared of anything, least of all what other people think. She's not scared of poverty – she's been poor. She's not scared of abundance – she's been rich. She's not scared of abuse – she's been vilified and gaslit. She's not scared of death – it's not the end of the road. She's not scared of mental illness because she's surrounded by people in all states of mind. She's not scared of being burgled because she's been robbed so many times she has the local cop shop on speed dial. She's not scared of black people, or white people, or brown people. She is only scared of God. Mona's life revolves around doing the work of the Lord, and anybody who would like to complain about it can eat a piece of chicken, sit down and listen.

A week ago, I called her to ask after Nabil's leukaemia. Mona was at Bunnings buying a jumbo bag of bird seed, to feed her pigeons. The landlord has told her that she can't feed the birds. The neighbours have complained. The birds are noisy and messy and flappy. 'Pests, not pets,' he said. When I mentioned this, she laughed slowly and said, 'But they're hungry, Sita-koo.'

Mona moves through life with more conviction than a monk, but significantly less restraint.

The door swings open and there she is. Her curly grey hair is tied with a satin scrunchie in a tight knot on the top of her head, and she's wearing a faded orange muumuu with brown turtle print, frilled at the neck and sleeves. On her wide, tanned feet are a pair of black orthopaedic sandals, the ones old ladies buy at the chemist. Little plastic nubs on the soles. Her dress has a gape down the side, where a seam has come loose, and if she sat down, anyone could see her large cottony knickers through the gap. In her left hand, she is strategically kneading a glob of pulverised oniony meat.

'I'm making kebabs. Nabil, go and check the fire not too hot,' she orders, pushing past him to me.

'Sita-koo!' She beams, as if she has seen a goddess in the flesh, not an exhausted mother of three who has just stepped off a cheap flight into an ecological sauna. 'Look! So beautiful you are! So tall!'

I kiss her sweaty cheeks, both sides, and bend down as she folds me in, keeping her left elbow out so I'm not pasted with raw meat. I breathe in her olive-ness, her pillowy softness. She pulls back and looks into my face. Her hawk-eyes regard me, unblinking. She says, 'We talk, Sita-koo. We talk.'

Mona's years of living among Torres Strait Islanders and the tribes of the North Queensland countries have given her middle-Indian accent a slightly ockerish drawl. Over my shoulder she shouts at the kitchen, 'Nabil! You not goin'. Stay and eat my kebab!'

'I gotta go, Ma,' he says, kissing her cheek as he moves past us and out the door, used to brushing off violent offerings of sustenance. 'I'll see you later. You all all right? If you all need anything, you just call me okay?'

'We all right. See you later then, jaanam.'

I feel a surge of affection for Nabil, and his defiant tufts of hair, and his worn t-shirt, and his shitty car. Men who look after their mothers are the lions of this world.

'Shut the door, Sita-koo,' Mona orders, 'and lock it up good. Put your bags in the first room there. Is it hot? Put on the air! Put on anything you want . . .' She potters back to her sizzling meat.

I bolt the door and take a look around her little home. The front door leads into a small, tiled family room that's set up like a dentist's waiting room, with couches and chairs lined up against every wall, and an open space in the middle. The curtains are a shouty green, with jagged tribal patterns in red, black and yellow, and the chairs and couches are a mish-mash of styles. There are cushions, no two the same, scattered artlessly about – some Indian paisley, some Turkish, some worn, plain cotton. Garage sale chic. Mona's walls are covered in posters and pictures, all blu-tacked in rows, like an information booth at a university open day. A university of God. Posters declaring the 'Oneness of God' and the 'Unity of Mankind' shine in multi-coloured splendour. Laminated coloured prints with quotes from the holy books, numbered with a Nikko pen, as if to encourage an order of recitation, or a group discussion. Against the far wall there are shelves and a cabinet overflowing with Bahá'í books and pamphlets, notepads and stationery. In the corner – a basket filled with tightly rolled up scrolls of paper, tied with ribbons. I move to the wall and read the poster closest to me – a picture of an oak tree in the shape of a heart. It says:

'Love is a light that never dwelleth in a heart possessed by fear.'

I pull my suitcase down Mona's tiny hallway and into the first bedroom. It's snug, but there is an air-conditioner. I freshen up, change out of my jeans and into a comfortable summer shift and thongs, and pad out into the hall again, peeking into the other rooms. Mona's room has a single bed with a bedside table, a sewing machine, a filing cabinet, a commode and a small couch piled high with fabric, sewing baskets, books and other things. It's haphazard but homely, and it smells like old cotton and moth balls. Her curtains are bright red, and squirreled away on a corner of the rumpled and worn bedcovers is a tight pile of liquorice-black fluff that turns out to be Mona's cat – a shy little beast that rolls itself up even tighter when I scratch his neck.

In the kitchen, the kebabs are still crackling, and I see that Mona has already fried a giant pile of them, tipping them onto a plate lined with paper towels. She hands me the spatula and wipes her hands on a kitchen towel. 'Sita-koo you cook? Only one more lot left!'

'Of course, Aunty. I'll do it.'

'Okay you do it then. Make sure they nice and done before you pull 'em off. I make 'em chai for you, and we sit down a bit.'

Aunty Mona's chai preparation certainly doesn't maintain the production values of Aunty Mehri's. It's much less complicated, and much less delicate. Utilitarian. A decent, strong builder's tea with no mucking about. Plain mugs fished out of the dish rack, black tea in a bag, a scoop of sugar, and some milk after it's brewed. She pulls some nân out of the fridge – it's Turkish, with black nigella seeds and white sesame. A couple of slabs are tossed into the toaster. She pulls butter and strawberry jam out of the fridge, while I fry the kebabs.

I pierce a hot kebab with a fork and take a nibble. 'Aunty, I think these need some salt.'

'Put it on then! I never know if it's enough. I just cook 'em and people eat. Sometimes they come good, sometimes no good. You fix 'em up, Sita-koo.'

I generously salt and fry the remaining kebabs, cover them with foil, wipe down the stove and toss the pan and spatula into the soapy sink. Mona has made four slabs of jam toast and two teas and is sitting down at her small dining table, peering at a book over her half-moon specs.

She closes the cover and says, 'Now you tell me, Sita-koo. Why you come to see me?'

'I just missed you, Aunty.'

Mona laughs and it rises. Bread in an oven. 'Good girl. I missed you too, jaanam. Come on, we have some kai-kai.'

I wipe my soapy hands on a threadbare tea towel and meet her at the table.

'Pray first, Sita-koo. Your soul need to eat. Just like your body. Before you give your body food, you gotta feed your soul,' she says.

I sit down opposite Mona, put my hands in my lap and say a little prayer – one I said often in my youth:

'Is there any remover of difficulties save God?

'Say: Praised be God! He is God!

'All are His servants, and all abide by His bidding.'

Mona smiles at me when I'm done, takes off her specs and lets them hang from her neck. This seems the perfect opportunity to start unpacking my suitcase of worries at her feet. But she doesn't ask why I've come all the way up to Cairns on one week's notice, nor does she pry into my marriage, or ask about Borhan, or the kids, or anything I actually want to talk about, things I need to talk about, things I have flown 1700 kilometres to talk about.

Instead, she dunks one jammy slab into her hot tea with the elegance of a storm trooper, slurps it up, and says while chewing: 'Sita-koo, sit quietly. I wanna tell you a love story like you never heard before.'

A love story like you never heard before.

Nestled in the crooked elbow of the Mimosa River, on the lands of the Wadja and Gangulu Peoples, is a small town called Woorabinda, meaning Kangaroo Camp. The story of the town is steeped in the dusty roads that border it, the brown grasses, the sandy soil and eucalypt roots. A history of war, sadness, pain, disease and displacement; a history of Aboriginal children stolen from their homes and relocated to tin and pale dormitories to be raised white. To have the devil and the brown bred out of their skin. But above the soil of Woorabinda, in the wattled air and the blue trees, something else simmers.

Mona says that sacrifice is a magic we can't understand. She says it transforms things. A seed sacrifices itself to become a tree. The seed is destroyed, but the spirit of the seed remains, infusing the tree's flowers and bark and leaves with its essence. The soil and the river and the brush grasses of Woorabinda are thick with the sacrifices of the Wadja and Gangulu People. That country heard the prayers and incantations of a thousand mothers, aunties and grandmothers who wept and wailed to see their babies through the bars of the settlement gates; the war cries of fathers left without sons; the trembling whimpers of children made longing, alone and afraid. It heard them and transformed them. Now something else sits there in their place. Mona says it is love.

Like most Parsi women of her generation, Mona married young and had babies fast. It wasn't an arranged marriage. Karim was tall, brooding and devilishly good-looking. He had beautifully coiffed hair, large hands and a moustache like an Indian general. Mona was enamoured with him – the deep and pulsating devotion of a nineteen-year-old girl for a handsome, worldly, older man. She was also wild and jealous, and devoutly committed to her faith. Karim loved to gamble and flirt, and

Mona loved to teach people about God. She wanted to travel to foreign lands, shouting the word of the Lord, and he wanted a wife who would stay home and make him panipuri.

When Karim turned thirty, his moods began to shift and swing. They were more black and white than before. Mona noticed, but she didn't know what was wrong. She made sure they stayed close to family. After Neymat died and Khodi left, Mona and Karim emigrated to Australia. For a decade they lived a hurricane life, pushing and pulling at each other like a frayed rope and anchor fighting the seabed. Karim wanted to know Mona's every movement. He wanted to know where she had been, with whom, doing what, and why. And then he wanted to fight about it.

One afternoon, after a particularly heated argument in the hazy light of a Brisbane summer, Mona decided to step out of the storm. She loved Karim, but she made her mind up to leave him. Not to divorce him – just to leave his house and his arguments and his vices.

Mona packed up her six children and hopped on a train going north to the sugarcane fields of Mackay, with no money, no house to go to, no job – just her kids and the number of a friend of a friend who would put her up for a few nights. When Karim realised his wife had left, he pottered around Brisbane for a bit, licked his wounds, and then went back to India.

In Mackay, Mona found a job as a cleaner and befriended a Bahá'í called Josiane. Josiane was a French woman with fabulous style and even more fabulous culinary skills. She was in the midst of a volatile break-up with a Frenchman called Jean-Paul.

Mona and Josiane became firm friends, and flatmates. She clucked and fussed over Mona's brood, cooking them pumpkin pie and ''elping them with their 'omework'. Mona thought Jean-Paul was très stupide et vaniteux, so she introduced Josiane to her tall and charming cousin, Farhang, who had come visiting to see if Mona and the kids were okay. Very soon, Jean-Paul was history and Josiane was part of the family. Mona cleaned houses, enrolled her children in the local state school, and prayed. She was poor, but she wasn't hungry or cold, and her children were happy.

One winter day, which in Mackay is like summer in most other places, she came home and told Josiane that she was tired of praying. What she really needed was to go teach the faith. She felt the call inside her and she had to go. Mona had been reading her copy of *The Bahá'í Bulletin* cover to cover, and she had seen that there was only one Bahá'í in a place called Woorabinda. She liked the name, how it sat in her mouth and rolled on her tongue. Woo-rrah-been-dah. She wanted to go. Josiane said she was 'appy to look after the children for a few days.

Mona called the secretary of the Local Spiritual Assembly of the Bahá'ís of Mackay, and found out the name and phone number of the one Bahá'í living in Woorabinda – a Mr John Spottiswoode. That evening she dialled the number. A deep and resonant voice answered the phone, greeting her in perfect Arabic.

'Alláh-u-Abhá!'

Mona felt Mr John Spottiswoode's voice fall into her throat like a cool glass of water. This was a voice that had flown on the tail of a kite from the marketplaces of Tehran. It was a warm piece of nân-e sangak on a cold morning, an oasis in the dunes of the Dasht-e Kavir.

From the scented bazaars of Persia to the mountains of India, 'Allah u Akbar' (God is great) or 'Subhan Allah' (how pure is God) are common greetings. A way to say 'hello, my friend' or 'goodbye, go well'. Anywhere in the East these salutations would be as usual as bread and butter, but to make a phone call to a remote Indigenous Australian settlement and hear an Aboriginal man answer in perfect Arabic: 'Alláh-u-Abhá!' This was like finding a fire in an igloo, or a butterfly in a mine.

Mona spluttered out a brief conversation, which ended in an arrangement to visit Woorabinda and help John with a barbecue he was organising for some locals the following weekend. He would pick her up from the bus stop.

For the next week, Mona thought about Mr John Spottiswoode. She wondered about him and his story. She wondered how a Black man knew the words of the East, and how big and tall he must be if his voice was so deep. She wondered if he was an Aboriginal man, or an Islander from the Torres Strait. She wondered what he did for a job, and what he ate. Should she take sandwiches? Or rice and curry? Or perhaps he would like some lamb kebabs? In the end, she just took herself.

When Mona arrived at the bus stop in Woorabinda, she wasn't greeted by an Aboriginal man. In fact, she wasn't greeted by a Black man at all. John was as white as any Scotsman in Glasgow. He was broad and firm, with a fierce bush of dark beard, eyebrows to match, and a voice like the ocean. Mona was so accosted by the sight and the sound of him, she stared at him all the way home and didn't say a word.

Over the next six months, Mona visited Woorabinda six times, and each time she became a little less scared of Mr John Spottiswoode, and more curious. He was a socioeconomic community development officer in Woorabinda. Mona had no idea what that meant. He had ideas about the environment, economy, politics and religion, and how they could work together to create thriving communities. He could talk to anyone. Black people, brown, white. They all respected him. Admired him. He was a magical communicator. He read constantly. He spoke fervently about permaculture, land management, settlement design and other things Mona didn't know anything about. But he spoke with passion, and a deep sense of spirituality. That, Mona understood.

On her sixth visit, Mona walked home down the dirt road that weaved through the centre of town, surrounded by Aboriginal children chattering and laughing. Twilight was coming on, and John was walking a few lengths ahead of her with some men from the barbecue they'd just had, his legs white and stocky next to their brown, lithe limbs. The light of the sky was tangerine and pink. It cast the blue-gums purple and spun the running creek to gold.

Suddenly, in the distance just past John, Mona saw something shining on the horizon. It was sparkling and hovering in the sky. She stopped walking and narrowed her eyes. She saw that it was an arrow.

The arrow cut through the air, leaving a golden trail in its wake. Mona stood still and watched it in earnest, wanting to cry out but unable to move. The golden arrow flew towards her, swift and sharp, and it hit her directly in the heart. Mona grabbed her chest in pain, thinking she had been hit, but there was no blood, no wound. Instead she felt something she had never felt before. It was overwhelming and strange and wonderful. It was an awe-inspiring torrent of love.

Before she could even piece together her feelings, there was another arrow. This time it soared through the sky and hit Mr John Spottiswoode. It hit him in the right ear. Mona saw him flinch and rub the side of his head, and turn to look back at her. For a minute their eyes met, but he showed no recognition of what had happened.

'Aunty,' I interrupt. 'Have you heard of Cupid?'

'Stupid?' she replies.

'No, Cupid. It's a kind of mythical baby fairy thing that shoots . . . never mind,' I say, 'go on . . .'

'Sita-koo, really it was amazing. You believe me. I not lying to you. I haven't seen 'em before and I haven't seen 'em again. They were golden and shining, and how they flew! And the love, jaanam!' She sighs and slaps her hand on her chest. 'It hit me. And then I knew.'

'Knew what?'

'I knew why we can't take our body to the next world when we die. Because the body not strong enough for that love. Only the soul.'

'Aunty, these arrows . . .' I say, now deeply invested, 'were they like something you would see in a dream, but you were awake?'

'Yes, like that.'

'I had a dream like that! A dream while I was awake – about Aunty Irie. I wanted to talk to you about it.'

She looks at me and smiles with a gentle glint.

'You already know,' I say flatly. 'Mum called you.'

'You are a dreamer, jaanam,' my aunt says. 'These things you see are like waking dreams. Now listen to me, because dreams are of two kinds. The first kind means nothing – maybe you eat too much or you run too fast and then you dream and it is rubbish in your head, just imagination-like. But the second type of dream is your soul connecting with the next world, the world of the spirit, and knowing things. The soul is the real you, not the body. Your body is like a cage, and your soul is like a bird. In the dream world the bird is free, and it goes and goes and goes. No bars. No walls. No time, even.'

'How do I know the difference between an indigestion dream and a soul dream?'

'Sometimes it a bit difficult, but you can tell it,' she says, watching me, narrowing her eyes. 'You can, can't you?'

I nod.

'Your grandmother was a dreamer. She got it in her too, like you. You lucky,' she smiles, and slurps her tea.

This isn't the first time I have had a waking dream. I'm loath to call it a 'vision' lest I be burnt at the stake with my own match, but when I was leaving Borhan, in the depths of my sorrow and fear, my grandmother 'came to me' while I was in the shower. I was standing under the hot stream, crying. It was indulgent crying. The type of performative weeping that makes you feel so sorry for yourself you weep even more. Snot was pouring out my nose. My eyes were red and running with tears and shower water, when I heard her laugh. She had an expansive, warm gale of a laugh. I recognised it immediately. I stopped sobbing and stayed very still, closing my eyes. She spoke to me as if she was standing beside me in the stall, as close as my own elbows. She told me that I was going to be very happy. That she couldn't wait to see how happy I was going to be. She said my tears were for nothing, and she laughed at my sadness. Her own laugh. And then she was gone and I heard the sound of the shower again.

That moment kept me going for months. But as it slipped further and further away from my memory, it felt like a madness. I wondered if it really happened. I thought perhaps it was my sorrow conjuring up a familiar, making up its own ghost. I couldn't tell anyone because they'd think what you're probably thinking. But now that I'm here, I can tell Mona.

She listens, eyebrows furrowed, chewing her bread in slow slaps.

'And why?' I ask her afterwards. 'Why is this happening to me? Maybe I'm going crazy?'

Maybe this is a kind of small insanity? I don't know.

'Why you so scared of everything?' she asks, tapping the table with one buttery finger. 'Let me tell you, Sita-koo, take that fear from your heart and chuck it away. Then you can fill it up with love.' Mona smiles expansively, as if her chest cavity is filling up with love. Then her face drops and sets. 'You think you put on this earth perfect? You wanna be perfect right now? No. You put here to learn.'

I open my mouth to speak, but she barrels on.

'You a school teacher. You know that the children learnin' nothing if they sittin' scared. That's you. You sittin' scared and learnin' nothing. That's why Irie came to you.'

'She came to me because I'm scared?'

'No. She came because you need to stop your thinking. "Don't worry. Be happy" means you thinking too far ahead, you thinking the future. What gonna happen? Am I gonna be all right? Is my kids gonna be okay? Right?'

I nod. She's right. I could think my way into the Bermuda Triangle and never return. I could overthink for Australia.

'You not mad, Sita-koo,' she laughs. 'Irie sent you here to me. She knows I never think ahead of anything. If I did, I wouldn't do it! You think I'd help those sniffers if I thought about it? You think I'd make a good business if I thought about all the things that can go wrong? You do like me now. Only think on what's in front of you. You feel much better.' She lolls back on her chair and nods her head with finality.

Blacky curls himself around her legs and jumps up onto the chair next to me. I scratch his fluffy ears.

'Did you fall in love with Uncle John that day, when the arrow hit you?' I asked, nursing the last of my tea.

'Oh no. I still scared of him then. But that love, that magic Woorabinda love. It went in us, and we couldn't fight it,' she says with a raised fist.

I can't help laughing. 'That was an excellent love story, Aunty.'

I make to move over to her, to kiss her cheeks soundly and wrap my arms around her neck. But she gets up, shuffling towards the kitchen. She reaches for a black plum and puts it into her mouth whole, sucking half off before pulling it out and saying, 'Sita-koo, be patient. We not up to the love part yet.'

Nine months ago.

I scoop a large spoonful of coffee ice-cream into my hot mug of instant Nescafe Blend. Make that two scoops. Actually, I'll just take the tub outside with me.

Brissy is heating up. The poinciana is covered in red and orange blooms. The magpies are having babies and tormenting small children on their walks home from school. Summer is coming. I sit in the cane rocking chair and look out over the trees above the creek, sipping my melty, cold-hot coffee.

It is obvious that I'm in love with the actor. It is also devastating.

He's in love with me too. I know this because he told me at noon on a Wednesday, before he left town. We were in bed at the lodge in Highgate Hill and he looked to me and said: 'Sita, not even bullshitting you. I'm in love with you.'

'I know,' I replied. 'I love you too.'

Fairly solid evidence.

We have known each other for twelve weeks. Two weeks ago, he went back to Sydney to workshop a new musical. We speak every night. We text during the day. It was easy to fall in love with him, like sitting with my back to the sun, or running my hand through sand. We slid into it. But I don't want it. What I want is to enjoy my lovely little romance, my sweet fling, with my bullshit over here and his bullshit over there. I want to enjoy it without the torment of something as wholly acute, incapacitating and violent as love.

Love means commitment and sacrifice and compromise. Love means worrying and keeping track and caring. Love means apologising.

I simply do not have time for this shit.

Borhan has just sold his house. The house we last lived in together. The house the kids love. He has decided on a tree change. It's been coming for years, but I never thought he would actually do it. Now he has. He's moving out west. He's bought one thousand acres in Traprock country. There's no house on the property. There are fields of blue grass, scrub, copses, forests of tumbledown gum and cypress pine, a winding creek, a dam, a stockyard, two large water tanks and an industrial-sized tin shed. There is no power. There is no plumbing. There is no toilet.

There is no toilet.

'What about the children?' I ask him, wild with indignation.

'Anyone who wants to come on this adventure with me, can come.'

'What about school?!'

'They can do distance education.'

The boys are already packing their bags. They haven't been this enthusiastic about an offer since we said they could have a puppy. Layla is incredulous. The idea of endless camping does not appeal to her. She's more the Fender-Jag, caramel macchiato, mosh-pit type.

'What about me?' I ask, tearing up.

'You want to come?' he replies, surprised. 'You're welcome to come, if you want to.'

'Of course I don't want to come!' I spit. 'I mean, when will I see the boys?'

'Seets . . .' he says with infuriating serenity, 'we will work it out.'

Now, not only am I in love, but I am in shock. Both at once. As my year ten literature class would say when presented with twenty pages on the sociological links between Stephen King's horror tropes and the cultural fears of contemporary America: This is not a vibe.

I slurp up a half-melted, oozy chunk of ice-cream and roll through my options. I won't tell Fari yet. About any of this. As for my aunts . . .

Irie would want details: 'Who is this man you love? Tell me everything. Of course he is in love with you! Any man would be in love with you. Is he handsome? What does he do with his life? Do you want me to talk to him? Let me talk to him.'

Mona would be adamant: 'Pray first. Then wait for answers to come. Sita-koo, pray first. You can't control men. You can only control yourself.'

Mehri would shrug and say, 'You open your door to wolves, you get eaten. Go cook something and forget about this boy. Unless you want to marry him. Do you want to marry him? If

you want him then marry him. If not, shut the door. And as
for your boys . . . boys follow their father. Let them go. They
will come back.'

Dolly would squeeze my cheek, fry me a paratha and serve
it up with a mound of butter and a hunk of tandoori chicken
– the most appealing option by far.

I spoon another lump of ice-cream into my coffee.

Marry him? Absurd. Never. Never again. I don't care what
God has to say about it. Anthony is not the marrying kind,
either. He's a living-in-sin kind of bloke, which is just one of
his many charms.

Let the boys go?! Just let them go? What about their friends?
Their community? What about how much I'll miss them when
they're hours away in a tin shed in the middle of the bush?

A large papa magpie lands on the balustrade. He gives a
throaty warble, eyeing me with suspicion.

My phone buzzes. It's Anthony.

'Hey babe, interesting news . . . my Sydney show has fallen
through. Covid-cancelled.'

'Shit. I'm sorry.'

'Don't be. I loathed it. I'm an impostor in musicals, anyway.
In the meantime . . .' he pauses for a breath. 'How would you
feel if I moved in on Friday?'

Only fools think they can stop love. Like it obeys the laws of
motion or the ordinances of time. I could no more stop myself
falling in love with Anthony and wanting him to be around me
than I could stop Borhan from falling in love with the dream
of a new life, or the boys from following their dad to the bush.

You can worry, you can overthink, you can pray to ease your soul and calm your mind, but you can't rope your life from the other side of the fence and expect to drag it into the stockyard. You have to stand back, watch the beast, admire it for its majesty and beauty and strife, and then muster up the courage to enter the arena.

I told Anthony that Friday would be perfect. Then, I helped my two sons pack their things, and I let them go.

A love story like you never heard before: Part 2.

Within a year of meeting him in Woorabinda and having golden arrows of love shoot through the air and into her heart, Mona divorced Karim by post, and married John Spottiswoode.

John had money. More money than Mona had ever had. Together, they scooped up Mona's kids and lived a good life together. They travelled. They stayed in fancy hotels. They ate well. They were happy. They were in love.

John and Mona moved to Thursday Island, a small island off the tip of Cape York – the most northern point of Australia. John loved to fish. He bought an enormous sailing yacht to take out onto the reef and beyond. He pulled in giant trevally, mackerel and Atlantic bluefin tuna, sometimes even a turtle or two, or some crabs. Mona did not love to fish. She was bored on the island. She wanted to work, but John said, 'No. We don't need the money, and the Island people need the jobs. If you work here, you'll be taking a job away from them.'

Instead of working, Mona sewed. She knew the kinds of dresses the island women liked to wear – long and bright and floating, with plenty of room for large hips and large breasts to breathe. Mona sewed frocks for the women, school uniforms for the kids, and shirts for the men. Then, she turned her sights to the tourists. Mona had t-shirts printed that said the names of all the Torres Strait Islands, with a big hibiscus flower on the side. She sold them out of a tiny room in town where people could call for a taxi. It was no bigger than a bathroom.

Mona knew when to fawn over customers and when to back off. She helped ladies try on her clothes and told them how beautiful they looked. If someone wanted something special, she made two different colours for them to choose from. Nothing was too much trouble or out of reach. Within one year, Mona was doing such a roaring trade she was able to move out of her tiny room and buy a large shop. She called it 'Mona's Bazaar'.

The bazaar sold dresses and shirts and sarongs, but also gifts and jewellery. Opals, black island coral and pearl shell. 'You can't get this nowhere else,' she told tourists. 'This is special Thursday Island jewellery. From our water.' They bought in bulk. Within five years, Mona had become the richest and most famous woman on the island, and John had been able to retire from his job at the Aboriginal Development Commission permanently.

That December, a tropical cyclone blew up over the reef and sank John's yacht, and Karim moved to the island.

Karim was resigned to his wife's new marriage. As Mona said to John, 'Karim didn't want me. He just didn't want anyone else to have me.' In fact, Karim found John, with his love for marine biology, diving, permaculture, science fiction and Indigenous affairs, fascinating to talk to. John found Karim a man of the world, with a terrific sense of humour. The two men became friends.

After all the absent years, Karim managed to win the war inside himself. He softened with age, and any edges that were left on him were sanded smooth by the island. He wanted to be with his children, as tall as they had become – to talk to them, help them, support them. He wanted to mend what was broken. And for a few years, until the cancer took hold, that is exactly what he did.

But, like a wisp of reed blowing in the island breeze, Karim became frail with sickness. Mona cared for him. She brought him food and drink, she showered him, she gave him his pills. She talked with him and prayed with him. His son and sons-in-law cut his hair, combed his beard and clipped his nails. His daughters sat with him and laughed with him and held his hands. He told them he loved them. He told them all the things he never told them before.

One morning in June, Mona went to check on him, taking sugared tea and bread to soak in it.

'Get out of here,' Karim whispered, his voice a hollow croak.

'What?'

'I'm telling you, Monavahr, get out! Leave me to myself.'

'Okay, okay. I'm going,' Mona said.

She put her hand over his frail, bone-fingers and said 'Alláh-u-Abhá, Karim.'

Then she left the tea on the stool and closed the door behind her.

Karim didn't want her to see him go. After everything that had been, everything they had seen on the broken road they walked together, he wouldn't have it. This was one trauma he could spare her. He died an hour later, alone.

Mona took care of the Bahá'í burial customs. With the help of two of her sons-in-law, she washed her ex-husband's body clean, wrapped him in white cloth, and pressed a burial ring engraved with 'God is the all Glorious' onto his finger. The next day, Karim was buried in the island cemetery, next to Japanese pearl divers and fortune-hunters, sailors and pilots. Those who had died naturally, and those who came to watery ends in the Coral Sea.

As his coffin was being lowered into the dirt, John Spottiswoode read the prayer for the dead. His booming voice was as wide as the ocean, just as Mona had first heard it over the telephone to Woorabinda.

'O my God! This is Thy servant and the son of Thy servant who hath believed in Thee and in Thy signs, and set his face towards Thee, wholly detached from all except Thee. Thou art, verily, of those who show mercy the most merciful.

'Deal with him, O Thou Who forgivest the sins of men and concealest their faults, as beseemeth the heaven of Thy bounty and the ocean of Thy grace. Grant him admission within the precincts of Thy transcendent mercy that was before the foundation of earth and heaven. There is no God but Thee, the Ever-Forgiving, the Most Generous . . .'

The saltwater breeze blew John's prayer through the long grass of the graveyard, down the hill and out to sea. Mona felt it washing her sorrow away.

What a parade it all is, she thought. Life. We sign documents promising us to one person, absolving us of another. We light candles and wrap ourselves in cloth or caps, we slide gold onto our fingers and tie our wrists together. Husband, wife, mother, daughter, father, son. Boss, employee, master, slave. We write the rules only for the next generation to cross them out and write different ones. We wear our costume and we play our part. But it's all a parade. We're in a parade of being human.

'In the end, it no matter, Sita-koo,' says Mona, pressing her thumb into the top of a soft orange and tearing it in two.

She peels the skin off and pushes the flesh into her mouth, handing me a juicy portion.

'The only thing that matters . . .' she says, her mouth full. 'The only thing that matters . . . is love.'

I bite into the orange. It's sweet and tender. The skin is thin.

'Aunty . . .'

'Yes, jaanam.'

'Did you ever feel guilty for divorcing Uncle Karim?'

'Never,' she said. 'Why should I? Why should my life be a sacrifice for one person? Why should anyone's?'

'It shouldn't.'

'That's right, Sita-koo. It shouldn't. Your life can be a sacrifice for many. But not for only one. You remember that.'

Six months ago.

'So, my mate Tom wrote a book.'

'Which mate?'

'Tom Tilley. Mudgee boy. We played rugby, did some musicals. We had a band called Spoon. A mix of Beatles and Grinspoon covers, few gigs at the PCYC. Pretty grim. He's doing a talk at Avid Reader next week. I think you might be interested.'

Anthony is chopping vegetables and placing them into neatly lined up little bowls on the kitchen bench.

'Sure. What kind of book is it?'

I scoop up my laptop and perch on a stool at the bench. The radio is tuned to Smooth FM. Soft rock central.

'It's a memoir. About him leaving his church.'

He spoons chopped onions into a buttery pot. They jump and pop and settle to sizzle. He takes a sip of his cab merlot.

'You want a splash, hun?'

'Sure.'

Anthony pours a slug of wine into a water tumbler and slides it across the bench. In goes the celery and garlic. A cursory stir. 'When we were growing up, I knew he was religious. I mean, he didn't swear, he didn't drink – that's about as shrewd as my observations got at the time. But I think there might be more to it.'

'That's When I Think of You' by 1927 announces its presence on Smooth FM.

'Tuuuuuuune. Volume, my love.'

I turn the radio up and smile at Anth's arse, popping like Beyonce's. He spoons the carrots into the pot, fries the mince next, Travolta-shimmies over to the sink to rinse the bowls.

I google 'Tom Tilley Avid Reader' and buy two tickets.

It's pissing down. It's been raining for a week. We catch an Uber to Avid Reader, a sweet little bookstore in West End, nestled in a strip of shops between the 7-Eleven and the Chinese restaurant. The pavement outside is soaked and puddling, but inside it is warm and dry and there's a tiny bar set up for the evening. We grab a wine each and meander, browsing the low tabled stacks, waiting for the event to start.

My favourite thing to do in bookstores is read first lines. To pick up a book, finger the binding and cover, open the first page and see what the author thought about for months – the very first sentence of their masterpiece.

> This unlikely story begins on a sea that was a blue dream, as colorful as blue-silk stockings, and beneath a sky as blue as the irises of children's eyes.
>
> —*Flappers and Philosophers*, F. Scott Fitzgerald

> For many years he had lived withdrawn from the world in which he had once played so active and even turbulent a part.
>
> —*The Letter*, Edith Wharton

Whether I shall turn out to be the hero of my own life, or whether that station will be held by anybody else, these pages must show.

—*David Copperfield*, Charles Dickens

We're ushered into a small back room to watch the interview. The fold-out chairs are snugly pressed together in short rows. Anthony and I are the last in and we have to shuffle into two tiny seats in the middle of the second row. With my long legs and his broad shoulders, we look like the last two crayons stuffed into a full box. Tom sits on a tiny stage, next to the interviewer. He's handsome. Tall and blond and straight-jawed. He grins an old-pal grin at Anthony, who grins back.

Tom grew up in a country town and was a member of a charismatic Pentecostal sect – the Revivalist Centre. His memoir, *Speaking in Tongues*, is about his doubts and his eventual departure from his fundamentalist faith. His shame, his turmoil, his family, his redemption, his spiritual and social emancipation, his search for community outside of faith. It's all there.

He speaks well. Draws the audience in with easy charm. Ten minutes into the interview, he mentions feeling embarrassed about teaching his faith to non-believers, in his youth. He says he never really felt comfortable 'witnessing'. My eyes begin to fill. I blink the tears back. He speaks about how it felt growing up in one big extended faith-family, and then how it felt to lose that family. I swallow and breathe slowly through my nose as I'm drawn back to a world where I played so active and turbulent a part. He speaks about the ache of disappointing his parents. My nose is running. I feel for a tissue in my bag. Nothing, not even a receipt. He speaks about his departure from faith, his unlikely story, and how it brought with it a deeper understanding of other people that the church considered 'worldly' or 'ungodly' – ships he had previously only seen from a distance – bohemians, artists, dancers, homosexuals, intellectuals, musicians. He learnt on his travels that these were some of the world's most wonderful, good, charitable souls. He felt as though he had found his tribe, and found himself sailing on a sea that was a blue dream. I hold back full sobs. He talks about letting go of salvation, and how he boldly chose to be the hero of his own life.

Alarmed at the state of my uncontrollably leaky face, I look towards the exit. There are too many obstacles to navigate between me and the door. Anthony catches my eye and puts his hand on my knee, squeezing it. He is fighting a different battle. It's warm in this small, congested room, and he runs hot at the best of times. Early on in the talk, Tom made a sweet and nostalgic reference to Anthony, which quickly turned heads and drew attention to him. His scalp began to rain. Now, he's sweating like a meat pie in plastic. He wipes his forehead incessantly with his hands. I wipe my eyes and nose with the inside sleeve of my sweater. We wipe in tandem. Two sweaty, snotty, leaky crayons.

Mercifully, the interview ends. I leave Anthony to press Tom's palm and make my way through the small crowd, step-ping out into the cool, rainy street. I twist my loose hair up into a top knot. I light a cigarette. A passing druggie asks if he can have one.

'Sure, no worries.'

'How's ya night goin', love?' he drawls, trying to strike up chat. I don't have enough kindness for myself tonight, let alone West End's nonsense. I give him the dart and turn my body away. He gets the point and wanders out into the rain, over the road. He sits outside The Bearded Lady. There's a saxophone playing inside. Paper moon.

Anthony emerges from the bookstore, package in hand.

'I got it signed to you.'

I take the copy of the book with a half-smile.

'Thank you.'

Here's the thing about doubt. It starts as a seed and it grows into a prize-winning gourd. When I started doubting my faith, I started doubting everything. If the foundation of your entire life is possibly a lie, then what else is? It's all up for grabs. Marriage, divorce, parenting, capitalism, free-range eggs, the royal family. All suspect.

I consider myself a professional doubter. I've been sitting on the fence for ten years. If I was doubting for the government, I'd be able to access my long-service leave and go on a holiday to the Costa Brava; have myself some time wearing big sunglasses, sipping sangria and watching Catalan sailors pass by the local Chiringuito. Not that there's anything glamorous about not knowing which team you belong to. The impostor syndrome, the waking up at 2am in an anxious sweat, the dreams about running for my life where my legs are sandbags and I can't scream. Come to think of it, it's a lot like being a writer. Perhaps that's why I seem to be settling so easily into the profession.

I'm most jealous of certitude. All around me people have it. People are so very sure of themselves.

Christians are sure. They're sure that Jesus is God and that Jesus died for their sins and was resurrected and will come again. Muslims are sure. They're sure that Mohammad is the last in a long line of Prophets to receive revelation from God. Even the Jews are sure – they're sure that the Christians and the Muslims are wrong. But do you know who are the surest of all? The most aggressively confident that they are 100 per cent correct? Atheists. Atheists are really, really, really sure. They're positive we've all been duped. And who knows? They may be right.

Where is the Church of the Holy Apostle of Not Friggin' Sure? That congregation I would like to join. Just after I attend Doubters Anonymous. (We go, we sit, we sip wine or whisky, we eat meat that isn't Halal, we pray for forgiveness and we talk about how we can't talk about anything.)

I read Tom's book that night in the privacy of my room, where leaking is regularly managed without public embarrassment. I read it from start to finish. About two chapters in, I started highlighting passages that I could have written myself. Even though the faith I'd been raised in was nowhere near as fundamentalist or strict or ritualistic as the Revivalist Centre's brand of Pentecostalism, I felt many of the moments that he described had been moments of my own. I never named them.

I'd never even spoken them out loud. But hearing someone else name them was bringing me undone.

Over the past ten years, I had managed to slowly step away from my faith community, without making a big deal about it. I certainly didn't leave the faith. Why would I? I had no idea what I truly believed about God or religion, and for all I knew, I could be horribly wrong. Led astray by unbelievers. Instead, I moved cities, I stopped keeping in touch, and I compartmentalised my life completely.

If I went back home, or saw my family, I never drank, smoked or swore. If they sat down to pray together, I sat down with them. If I was asked why I wasn't participating in Faith activities, I just pretended that the kids had kept me too busy. But when I went out with my secular friends, it was a different story. I allowed myself to do all the things I had never done in my teens and twenties. I partied. I never mentioned my faith. I did as I pleased – drinking, smoking, toking, dating, going to bars and clubs. I pretended that God didn't exist.

I was two in one.

2000. Brisbane.

My Nokia buzzes. A text from Jamal.

Seets. You home? I'm coming round.

I put down the hairdryer and the barrel brush, pick up my mobile and call him.

'Jum, I'm home but we're about to head out.'

My girlfriend Janie and I are going to the Royal Exchange in Toowong to meet up with some of our friends from uni. I'm wearing a fuzzy, scarlet boat-neck top and low, low hipster jeans. I want to be Liv Tyler. It takes approximately seventeen hours to part my long, wavy hair down the middle and blow dry it straight to look like hers. The 2000s are torturing us all with jeans that barely cover our pubic bones but are so long the tattered hems drag on the ground. I've just waxed the bottom of my tummy and back so that the two-inch strip of bare midriff between my top and jeans will look smooth and sexy. It doesn't. It looks red and aggravated. Maintaining some form of allure in this high-grunge climate is a daily struggle.

'I'm walking up your stairwell now,' he says.

Janie and I live in a cheap seventies apartment building near the Milton railway station. The carpet is creamy shagpile. The tiny-tiled verandah has a low metal railing. In the kitchen there is an olive-green vinyl booth that was optimistically advertised as a 'breakfast nook'. We exist on a diet of tuna mornay and toasted baked-bean sandwiches.

I open the door to my brother, holding his car keys and smiling awkwardly.

'Come in,' I say, heading back to the bathroom. 'Talk to me while I finish my hair.'

'Seets . . .'

'What?'

Jamal sees Janie sitting on the couch, lacing up her Doc Martens.

'Hi, Janie. How are you?'

'Well, thanks. And you?'

'What is it, Jum?' I ask, exasperated. He's not even coming through the door. Just standing in the hallway like a Mormon.

'Seets, can you come out here for a minute, please?' he asks with a pointed glance at Janie.

I huff, chuck the hairbrush on the couch, and head out into the hallway with him. He pulls the door closed behind us. We're standing in the small, second floor landing. An updraught of cool breeze blows through from the stairwell behind me and up the other.

'What is it? You're being so weird.'

'Seets, it's Grans. She passed away this afternoon.'

I stare at him. We don't move. I hear the squeal of wheels on rail as the city train comes to a stop at Milton station. A drop of water from my wet hair drips onto my neck.

'Dad found her. He thought she was sleeping. She was in her chair. She went peacefully . . .'

'What?' I whisper.

He puts his arms out and I put out mine. My knees go from under me, but he catches me and lowers us both down onto the steps. My big brother pulls me in tight.

'It's all right. It's okay. You're okay, Seets.'

We sit there for ages, until my breathing steadies and the moment ties itself to the earth. Here it is, now.

'Pack a few things in a bag,' Jamal says. 'We're going home.'

Dolly is buried in a grassy field where the marble headstones are set flat into the soil. Around and about her grow camphor laurels and rose bushes, pine trees and ribbonwoods. In summer, the winds blow hot and dry, like they do in Tehran, and in winter the grass frosts with little glass beads of ice.

Four graves away lies her friend, Margaret Walker, Dad's mum, and two graves away from that her granddaughter, Rahnee.

On her headstone, words from her favourite prayer are etched in gold:

'IN THE GARDEN OF THY HEART, PLANT NOUGHT BUT THE
ROSE OF LOVE.'

BAHA'U'LLAH

2015. Brisbane.

'Do I just let it dissolve on my tongue?'

'Yep. We'll do it together. Ready?'

I nod and put the tiny square of paper onto my tongue. It has no taste and is gone in a second.

I look around the forest. We've veered off the dirt walking path and hiked down into a gully, crunching brown leaves, twigs and seed-pods under our feet. Above us is a sandstone outcrop. Borhan and I are standing in its shade.

Our talks about separating have led to this. A day off work to open our minds in the Toohey Forest. Borhan suggested it might be a good way for us to access our subconscious and deconstruct our years together. To open our heads and hearts to everything that passed between us. Commune with our higher selves. 'Consciously uncouple.'

Sounds reasonable.

I'm thirty-four years old. I've never taken a disabled parking spot. I've never stolen a packet of chewing-gum. I've never boarded the bus without swiping my *go* card, and I've certainly never accessed my subconscious under a sandstone outcrop of a state forest with a man I am about to divorce.

Borhan has explained how it all works, but I ask him to go over it again.

'You'll feel nauseous at first, maybe for a few minutes. You might feel a bit dizzy too, but we can sit down. Once the sick feeling settles, it will be amazing. You'll feel great. Just be open to the experience.'

We sit down on the forest floor. I play with the spindles of a grass tree. They are smooth and sharp, like long needles. The birdsong is intense. Miners, butcherbirds. Lorikeets and finches. The forest is swinging with calls and hoots. Under the cry of the birds is the buzz of insects. Grasshoppers, cicadas and bees, all choosing their own notes to hit. I pick at the tree with my fingernail. I close my eyes.

I feel nothing.

'Are you sure this stuff works?'

'Just give it a few minutes, Seets.'

I'm not really a forest type of gal. I mean, I like nature, but I prefer open, grassy fields and lone, large trees to mossy and dense understorey. It's the space. I like being on the edge of vastness. Here, we're surrounded by creepers, grasses and scrub, entwined and grabby, jostling for pieces of sunshine. Bridge Street was wide, all sloping clover-covered lawns and big trees. A jacaranda here, a camphor laurel there. When the wind blew you could really feel it hit you.

I'm feeling something now. Yes. I am definitely feeling something. Woozy. Like I've stepped off the tea-cup ride at a carnival. I lean over to one side and stare intently at the forest floor. I consider dry retching, but I close my lips instead. I lick them and swallow my saliva. A willy wagtail perches on a rock nearby and wags his tail at me. I stare at him. He's so black. Black as the night sky over Goondiwindi. Goondiwindi. Gundy. I went to a rodeo there once. I was sixteen and a man danced with me. A long-legged, sun-brown cowboy. I straddled his thigh as he swung me around. Blood rushed to my crotch. It felt like I'd done something wrong, so I pushed him away.

I watch the wagtail hopping from rock to branch for what feels like an hour, until the wooziness disappears. Blinking, I drag my eyes away from the bird and gaze at the eucalypt forest in front of me.

Holy shit. The trees are people.

I squeeze my eyes shut and rub them with my fingers. I look at Borhan. Is he a tree? No. He's still a person. He smiles at me. I look down at my hands and feet. I'm a person too. I stand up slowly to stare at the trees. They stare back. We watch each other, acknowledging one another with gentle nods. The people-trees still look like trees, but I know they are people on the inside. They are shades of green and yellow that I've never seen before. Bright and bold, but at the same time, mellow and subtle. Lemon and butterscotch, fern and pear.

I approach the tree closest to me. A tall, gnarly gum. He's low-voiced and old. He tells me I'm beautiful. I put my palm on his trunk. He calls me darling. My eyes widen. Is this tree flirting with me? We just met. I turn to Borhan.

'This guy needs to watch it.'

'Oh yeah?'

I wag my finger at the gum, smiling coyly. 'Cheeky. Verrrrry cheeky, mister.'

I walk over to a group of saplings and sit down at their feet. Young people. Talking among themselves. Not interested in me. I can hear little whisperings from behind rocks and clumps of dry leaves. Tiny giggles and murmurings.

Fairies. I'm in the Enchanted Wood.

Oh my god, I'm going to meet Silky and Moonface and the Saucepan Man! I'm going to get to eat pop-cakes and google buns and slide down the slippery-slip.

'Huh?' says Borhan.

'The Magic Faraway Tree. Where is it?'

'I don't know . . .'

'Let's find it! We will climb to the top and go to the land of topsy-turvy and the land of take-what-you-want.'

A fierce wind has blown me back into my past and I'm yelling like Johnny one-note. Into the trees.

'What?' He's laughing now.

I implore him to get up. We start hiking up towards the ridge. I'm looking around for the Magic Faraway Tree. I'm stopping to talk to eucalypts and grass trees and creepers along the way (all nice guys). The whole forest is magical to me. Alive with whispers and chuckles and tiny bells in chorus. I'm Alice in Wonderland. I'm through the wardrobe and into a frozen Narnia. I'm Pippi Longstocking.

We reach the walking path. There are two people, a man and a woman, going for a morning jog. I leap back from the path and pull Borhan with me. We hide behind a tree. We peer out and watch them stride past. Their legs are long, their torsos impossibly stretched, their skin bright, luminescent blue. Muscles ripple and bulge. I stare at their perfect faces. Their eyes, diamonds.

'It's the Na'vi,' I hiss.

'What?'

'From Pandora. Can't you see it? Don't move. There are others.'

Two more joggers pass. Both Na'vi. The forest is teeming with enormous blue people.

'Let's get away from the path,' I say.

We are light on our feet, like elves. We cross the path and continue up the hill. We come to a rocky, bouldered ridge and walk along it. I'm a tight-rope walker. I'm Mary Poppins. I'm Wendy and Peter Pan at once.

'Stay to the left of me,' Borhan says.

'I won't fall. I know what I'm doing. The tree has got to be around here.'

'Just stay over this side.'

'Okay.'

He looks normal. Unchanged. He isn't blue. I'm not blue, either.

I can't find the tree. It doesn't matter.

We come to a wide, flat rock and look out over the ridge. We are high up. The canopy moves in front of us in mint-greens and greys, sun-yellow and peach. A wattle is beginning to burst into bloom. The little yellow flower-puffs are floating and chattering to one another like tiny ballet dancers waiting in the wings. I stare at the ensemble as they prepare to dance. They jeté and pirouette in gold and honey and dandelion-yellow. I have never seen anything so glorious.

Inside my chest cavity, glowing and pulsing, I feel an over-whelming love for the artists in my life. The poets, the players, the dancers, the songbirds. I'm in love with them all. I'm proud of them all. I am them, and they are me. We are the same thing. The soul of the ballet-dancing wattle and my soul are no different. My chest caves inward, as I try to touch the love with my ribs.

'Let's stay here for a while, Seets.' Borhan's voice pulls me back to the flat rock. He lays out a blanket for us to sit on.

'Okay.'

'Close your eyes and tell me what you see.'

I close my eyes. A scene materialises on the backs of my eyelids.

I see a blue and green river. Ocean-blue. Pine-forest-green. It's flowing. It's so beautiful. It's Fari.

'I see my mum. She's a river!'

'She's in a river?'

'No, she is the river. It's her soul. Her soul is the river.'

I see another river running next to it. The same colours, flowing and gurgling.

'I see Jamal. He's a river too.'

A tree appears. It's growing out of a craggy mountain. The tree is robust. A large oak in oranges and reds, the leaves scarlet and apricot and tangerine. It stands alongside the rivers, with sturdy, wide branches that cover them. I see each leaf sway and blow in the breeze. The tree is my dad, and the mountain he is growing from, is his mother.

Another tree appears, on the other side of the twin rivers, opposite the John-oak. It is so beautiful. Blush and rose-pink, lavender and mauve leaves, with a mulberry-coloured trunk. A tall, strong willow. Its elegant branches leap and flow. It moves like silk, rustles like crepe paper. My sister, Lisa.

Above this scene is a rainbow. It's fat and bright and arches over the whole sky.

'Oh, I see Rahnee. She's a rainbow!'

'What are you?'

'Wait, let me look.'

I look around for myself in this scene, but I'm nowhere.

Something is happening. The rainbow is moving. The colours are bleeding into one another. It's disappearing from the sky. The rainbow dissolves and melts away until there is nothing left but grey. Grey clouds. Rolling thunder. Rain.

'It's raining. She's gone . . .' I feel my heart race. Panic taps at the edges of my eyes.

The rivers begin to run. They are flowing and rushing, faster and faster, the blue and green swirling against each other. They swell together to form one rushing current. The current grows. The banks are threatening to burst. Fari and Jamal, mourning, weeping. The water is rising. Soon it will flood. But, the trees. Look at the trees.

The two trees, the oak and the willow, John, Lisa, are leaning over the rivers, sheltering them. Together, they push their roots deeper into the ground, under the rushing flow. I can see the tips of the roots pushing down through the soft earth, fortifying the river bed and raising the banks. The trees are making sure the water stays the course. Deep underground they lock their roots and hold on. Above ground their branches blow and flutter in the curling wind.

'They saved them . . .' I say, my eyes darting to and fro under my eyelids, watching the scene unfold in technicolour. 'The rivers were going to rush away with sadness, but the trees saved them.'

The storm blows. The trees hold. The rivers run. I look up in the sky. One by one, the black and grey clouds are clearing, and behind them in the black sky, night now, there are fireworks. It's Dolly, and it's me. We are the fireworks. I'm a firework! Neon-pink and electric-blue and grape-purple. Bursting. Showing off. We are the same colours, moving and jumping and spraying light across the sky.

I look down. The fireworks are reflected in the river. The river watches the sparks of the fireworks flit and burst and dazzle, and for a minute, it forgets to run. Turn by turn the river slows. It holds its course. The wind is easing, the trees are still, the water runs with an easy tilt.

'I know what happened,' I say to Borhan, crying. 'I know what happened now. I can see it. I saw it.'

I'm shaking. My teeth chatter. All of a sudden, it's cold.

'You know what happened with us?'

'No, not with us. With them.'

Then, I weep. I weep for a long time. I let myself fall into it. Everything I had pushed down is drawn up, and out, and into the forest.

When I recover, we eat corn chips and grapes and drink some water. I laugh at the cartoonish crunch of the chips. I'm Goofy, crunching through a handful of peanuts.

'I wonder if you can see other souls,' Borhan said as we lay back on the blanket and looked up at the sky. 'Can you see the kids?'

I close my eyes and look for my children.

'Yes, I can see them.'

'What are they?'

'William is a rainbow, but not curved, straight – like a laser-beam. Layla is a river, like Mum and Jamal, and Leo is a burst of yellow sunshine.'

We laugh. We talk about our children. Our beautiful, funny, radiant children. We melt with love for them.

'Can you see me?' he asks.

I look for Borhan. I think about him. I imagine his face and his voice. All the messy years. All the good, and all the not so good . . . and there he is.

He is a ball of fire. Molten pops and slow-lava cover the surface of his sun. He crackles and burns and blazes. Red-hot and golden.

I open my eyes.

'I saw you.'

'What was I?'

'A ball of fire.'

'Fire? Like you?'

'Yeah.'

Fire and fire.

Too much fire.

Five months ago.

I leave work early. The traffic is easy. At home I check the mailbox and it's all junk and campaigning. The front door isn't locked. I kick some gumboots out of the way and come into the house without rattling the keys in the latch.

There's a sound. A low, guttural moaning. I stop dead to listen, and put my keys in the bowl slowly. I'm hyper-aware now, like all women who've lived alone. The moan bleeds into soft, sad, wounded cries. Mournful, animal sounds, on the edge of human, in that space where humans and animals meet. They're coming from my bedroom.

I move through the house quickly. I push open the bedroom door. Anthony is curled up on the bed. His limbs wrapped caul-like around the crumpled and worried doona. The blinds are closed. Chinks of burnt-orange afternoon sunlight fall through into a room that is filled with broken sadness.

I drop my bags on the carpet and crawl onto the bed, still in my boots. I bury my face into his. I kiss his damp cheeks and press my body to his side. I lay my thigh over him, pulling his shoulder in, turning his head towards me. He puts his arm around my waist and presses his face into my chest, keening.

I say his son's name. I ask if that's it. He nods.

'He's too little to be away from . . .'

I hold him. I tell him it will all be okay. I tell him life is long and always changing. Always. I move my hand in circles on his chest and back. I kiss his forehead. I run my hand over his head and his neck until his breath slows and meets mine and we are breathing together. I tell him how lucky his boy is to have a dad who misses him so much and loves him so deeply. A dad who tells stories and does all the voices, who makes him laugh and lets him be who he is.

I tell him that blood is thick and that it will hold.

Once the waves slow down, I move to get up. To get him a drink of water, or a glass of wine, hot milk, a club sandwich. Anything to ease a broken heart and soften the year's worth of grief that has just poured out of him.

I pull my hand away from his chest but he stops it with his.

'No. Lie with me. Stay.'

There are some women who enjoy the company of men, some women who distrust them, and some who have been so injured by their crimes that they cannot come to ever truly let them in. I love men. I adore them. I'm enamoured with their foolishness and their freedom, their strength and their great capacity to say 'no'. I love older men who have wrestled with ambition and learnt to rein in their pride, who can say sorry and mean it. I love young men, filled with arrogance and invincibility, who would take on the sun if it meant dying a hero's death.

The way my son kickstarts a dirt bike and ploughs down a country road, with nothing on his mind, just the wind and the growl of the bike and his almost-man, dusty hands wrapped around the grips. The way my baby boy pretends he hasn't noticed me watching and then does his best tricks on the trampoline. Showing off. Flicking his long hair. Wanting me to tell him how bold he is, how clever, how handsome, which of course, I do. I praise men much more easily than I praise women. Anthony says I give him the most absurd praise for doing nothing, that I say 'good on you, babe' if he irons a shirt or eats a chicken sandwich. I don't know why. I suspect Freud would have something to say about it.

Last week Anthony's boxes arrived from Sydney. He unpacked his books, his DVDs and, finally, more clothing. He's been on a four-shirt rotation for ten months. I came home to find him sipping port and reading a Harold Pinter biography in front of the heater, barefoot, in tracksuit pants and a Silverton Hotel trucker cap. I stared at the three shelves of well-thumbed books and on his life of rootlessness, with longing. The books were categorised: American drama, the Russians, UK plays. I pored over them. Fiction, memoir, some weird coffee-table stuff. A book of Leonard Cohen poems with the inscription *My darling heart, Happy Valentine's Day* inside the cover. Ted Hughes' book *Birthday Letters*. Scrawled on the first page, *A birthday book for a birthday man. Happy twenty-fifth you fucking fuck!* There was a photo album. I flipped through the pages of his rolling adolescence and early, bucking manhood. For a moment I felt a jealous despondence.

We're on the deck. There's a cold moon. The smell of cut grass and winter chill on the night. Our neighbour, Kris, is taking a phone call in his backyard, handling problems about trucks and freight and drivers. Problems we two could never solve. Over here it's all talk about character arcs and subtext and how the lighting and colour palettes in season three of *Ozark* reflect the shifting tones in the narrative. Earlier, we were bickering about who would be better in a trench warfare situation. Anthony was adamant we would both be shit. I maintained I'd be good in a trench.

'Darling. My sweetheart.' He said with furrowed brow. 'You'd be bloody awful. A real liability.'

'Rubbish! I'd bring a sense of humour and camaraderie to the team. Buoy the troops!'

'Sita. This isn't *Dad's Army*. We're talking severed limbs, exploding shells, gangrene. Your best friend's face a pile of goo dripping through your fingers. A letter from your sweetheart saying they couldn't wait and had babies with some prick down the street. No one is gonna give a fuck if you can tell a knock-knock joke.'

I contemplated this.

'I stand by it,' I said. 'I think I could handle a trench.'

He sat back in disbelief. 'You might *sneak* into the war room. Serving tea and biscuits to the admirals. At best.'

'Ooh admirals. That'd be nice.'

'Yeah babe. Little appreciative pat on the bum on your way out? Much more your speed.'

'And yours.'

'Depends who was cast as the admiral. Ooh, Patrick Stewart would be fab.'

We chuckled in regard of ourselves.

Right now, he's scrolling curmudgeon-like through his feed, muttering about 'snowflake actors' who brand themselves as angels sent from the heavens to illuminate the human race. 'Get a grip, people. Yes, love your work. Yes, make it vulnerable, make it ugly, make it transcendent. But then take off your bloody dress-up and go home and stop being a wanker.'

I'm a bit gloomy. Flinty. I don't take it up. 'Hm . . .' I reply.

'You okay?' he asks, putting his phone down.

I shrug. 'I dunno. I've been thinking about your photos. I'm a bit jealous, I suppose.'

He gives me the full blue-grey for a moment, then says, 'Seets. You are the love of my life. But I can't change my past.'

'No, no. I'm not jealous of your ex-girlfriends,' I tell him. 'I'm jealous of your wandering years. The richness of your life, your experiences.'

He brushes this off like a crumb. 'It was just plays and flings, hun.'

'Exactly.'

But he needs me now. He needs to orbit a true moon. A moon anchored in place by children. His life needs a steady pulse, now that he has a boy of his own.

I need him too. He makes the nights seem longer. He makes me laugh. He washes my kids' school uniforms, cleans the house and remembers when we need milk. He tells me I'm an incredible writer and should back myself. He tells me he walked under a lucky star and met the best person in the world.

His son comes to stay with us now, often. Anthony counts the sleeps waiting for him to arrive. My kids love his little boy and his little boy loves my kids. And when Anthony sits on our deck and watches his favourite person in this world happily bouncing on the trampoline in his Ghostbusters costume, he says this is what true happiness is. The happiest he's ever been.

He's a kind man with an artist's heart.

I hope we hold the road together for some time.

Three months ago.

'Perhaps, you need to tell them.'

'I can't. I don't want to hurt them.'

'They're your parents, Seets. Chances are good they know already.'

My friend Fiona is right. This is because she is really, really smart. A Doctor of Philosophy. Like bloody Socrates. Which is what you need when you're having a crisis of faith.

'Think of it as a conversation,' she says, 'rather than a confession.'

We are drinking the worst coffees in the world. Next to us on the bench are bunches of native flowers. Banksias, billy-buttons, gum leaves. Fi has a bunch of pink carnations tucked into her handbag.

I've just finished telling her about the Tom Tilley book, *Speaking in Tongues*, and the way I've felt since I read it. How the question of my faith has been dragged up to the surface and now it's sitting just under my skin, making me itch.

'Just have the first conversation of many,' she says. 'You don't need to cover everything in one day. Think of it as a process, not an event.'

So sensible. She is so sensible. She's master Yoda, and I'm Lucille Ball getting a pie in the face. But we click. Fi was my neighbour when I lived with Borhan on Sexton Street. We had a bucket attached to a rope pulley between our back decks. We sent things back and forth – tins of tomatoes, onions, bottles of beer. Her husband, Chopper, cut a hole in our fence and installed a little saloon door for the kids to go through. We all went on beach holidays together. Ate pizzas on Friday nights. Swapped newspapers.

'If you share with them what's going on with you, they will most probably be relieved. I don't think you're giving them enough credit.'

'I'll think about it,' I say, anxiously sipping my crappy coffee and changing the subject. 'Let's go get one of those weird bratwurst bowl things.'

'Or a "stroopwafel",' Fi says, wrestling her flowers into her arms. 'Whatever the fuck that is.'

That night I went home and prayed. I was alone in the house. I started with a book, but I found I remembered most of the prayers by heart. I didn't make requests. I didn't beg. I didn't plead. I didn't expect that God would hear me. I hoped instead, that I would hear God.

The next morning there was a text message from an old friend April Alizadeh. I hadn't heard from her in years. We used to bunk together at Bahá'í youth camps, but we drifted apart. Not on purpose, just life. She disappeared overseas and I forgot to think about her. But here she is now. Asking how I am. Telling me about her life. I find myself opening up to her. Like a little chunk of my past has come back to me, wrapped in muslin. I open it like a gift. I tell April everything.

Where I had rushed into a husband and kids, she had leant into her career. It had taken her all over the world, and she'd ended up in San Francisco. When I asked her if she was married, she said no. It turns out, men weren't for her. Instead, she had a beautiful partner, Elizabeth.

'How did your parents take that news?'

'They've come a long way over the past few years in their ability to hold multiple truths – our daughter loves the faith, is a Bahá'í, and also loves women.'

'Wow.'

'It's important to draw a distinction between loving some-one and pleasing them. You can love your parents and still disappoint them, or let them down. Sharing who you are, in all its beautiful complexity, and bringing them on the journey with you, is perhaps more important than their reaction. What you're feeling is very natural, Seets. It comes with the terrain of courage.'

The terrain of courage. *The terrain of courage.* Yesterday I was eating a stroopwafel and today I'm Joan of Arc.

The terrain of courage.

There it is. There's God.

I hear Mona's words come back to me. They fly in and circle around my head. Why you so scared of everything? Let me tell you, Sita-koo, take that fear from your heart and chuck it away. Then you can fill it up with love.

I hear Irie crushing spices. Nobody ever got anything they wanted by sitting quietly and waiting for it.

I hear my mother. Fari. My beautiful, silly, warm and good mother. Sita mine, in life we are all standing in a circle, holding hands. Whatever you give away will come right back to you.

What would I want my own daughter to do? What would I want coming back to me?

I will tell my parents the truth.

Two months ago.

'Why don't you just marry him and get it over and done with?'
Fari says, handing me a pile of dirty towels from the bathroom
floor. 'Take these down to the laundry.'

I'm back home for a visit, on the way out west to see the
boys. Layla is filling the bath for her grandmother. Lighting
candles. She throws in a flowery bath bomb and watches it
fizz. Squeezes in some lavender bubbles.

'My granddaughter loves making a spa for us,' Ma says,
stripping off her top.

'Ma, I'm not marrying him. We've known each other for ten
months. Do you really think that is a sensible choice? Really?'

'But he's living with you!' Off come her tracksuit pants.

'Yes. He is.'

'Grandma, get in,' Layla says. She's sitting in the bath in her
togs. She holds her hand out for her grandmother to take it.
Ma steps in, lowers herself slowly and sits facing Layla, their legs
knocking together, four knee-caps poking out of the bubbles.

'It's so hot . . .' Fari exclaims with a pleased sigh. 'How nice.
My favourite thing is a hot spa.'

She picks up a handful of bubbles and puts them on her
chin. She sings:

'There was an old man called Michael Finnigan.

He grew whiskers on his chin again.

The wind came up and blew them in again.

Poor old Michael Finnigan. Begin Again.'

Layla laughs and dries her hands on a towel, reaching for her iPhone. 'Grandma, Grandma, sing it again. I'll film you.'

'Okay but don't put my naked bod on your insta-pinsta!'

'Omigod. I won't.' (She absolutely will.)

I take the damp towels down to the laundry, passing my dad's book-lined office on the way. His door is closed. I drop the towels and knock.

'Come in.'

'Hey, Dad.'

'My precious treasure!' he says, swivelling his desk chair to face me. 'What brings you in here?'

'Your wife,' I say. 'She just told me I should marry Anthony. We've been seeing each other for ten months. It's madness, and I told her so. And I wanted to tell you too, in case you were of the same opinion.'

'Ah ha,' he said, hitting pause on the second movement of Mozart's concerto for flute, harp and orchestra in C major.

'I don't intend to marry again, Dad.'

'I see.'

'I don't want any more children. I don't want to share a bank account with anyone. I'm not interested in signing papers or changing my name or walking down an aisle. I've done all of that. And I know it's not the Bahá'í way – to live with someone you're not married to. But . . . I honestly don't believe that God cares.'

John listens with his chin tilted down, and then says, 'How about we have a cup of tea, dear? I need a break from these accounts, anyway.'

We head to the kitchen. I flick on the kettle while he pulls out two mugs. I can hear Mum and Layla larking about upstairs.

'You were saying,' he says, looking for some biscuits, 'you don't believe that God cares . . .'

This is the moment. It's time. Love is a light that never dwelleth in a heart possessed by fear.

I take a deep breath.

'I struggle with my faith, Dad,' I say evenly. 'I've been wanting to tell you for a long time that I'm struggling with it.'

He says nothing. Just watches me pour the boiling water into two mugs.

'You came upon your faith in such a revelatory way,' I continue. 'It's different for me. I've had this faith since I was born. I've been spoon-fed it. And now, I don't know whether I believe because I was taught to, or because I really feel it, you know? I don't know if I'm sincere.'

He's listening. John doesn't interrupt.

'One sugar?' I ask.

'Yes, please. And a splash of milk.'

I finish making the tea and push his towards him. We sit down together on the lounge.

'I used to be so sure, Dad. So, so sure. But everything that's happened to me makes me doubt it all.' The dogs next door bark at a passing cyclist. A flower opens up in my belly. 'My biggest worry is disappointing you and Mum. Because I love you both, and Mum's had enough sadness in her life.' My voice is shaking now. My lip quivers like an old hand in a loose wind. 'I don't want you to feel like I'm throwing my upbringing back in your face, Dad, because it was wonderful, and I'm grateful for everything you and Mum taught me, and did for me.' The flower blooms and bursts. Petals fall. I wipe my cheeks. 'And I know it's silly, but . . . I'm scared.'

'Scared?'

'I'm scared that if I tell you all this, you will love me a little bit less.'

John puts his cup down on the coffee table. I look at the carpet. Clear my throat. Sip my tea and try to swallow my feelings down with it. Through the lounge-room window I can see the lemon tree in the backyard is bending with the weight of yellow fruit. The bougainvillea covering the fence palings is budding into bloom. A currawong calls twilight in with a gallop and a sigh. Whip-o-whoo-why.

'Sweetheart . . .' he says, a small catch in his throat. 'As a Bahá'í, I believe that a person's faith is conditioned by no one but themselves. Your relationship with God is your business, my precious treasure.' He puts his hand on my knee and blinks his eyes. 'You have had tests in your life that have been very difficult, and affected you quite deeply, and those tests have led you here. Your journey will continue and I have no doubt you will work out how you feel about the world. No doubt. And I will be here to support you.'

I feel relief pour warm blood through my veins. John puts his arm around me, and pulls me into his chest. His enormous bear-paw rests on my shoulder. He pulls his neatly folded handkerchief from his top pocket and presses it into my palm.

'And I will always love you, my darling. No matter what you do.'

Layla and I step out of her dusty nineties model Nissan X-trail and stretch our legs, taking in the timber facade of the hotel. Balconied rooms are available above the pub. The heritage doors to the front bar are open. There's footy on the telly, the hoppy smell of beer, a couple of permanent geezers sitting at the window nursing cold ones and staring at the road.

We've just driven 282 kilometres west to get here, from Brisbane, with Layla at the wheel. She got her learner's licence and has to clock one hundred hours of driving before sitting for her final driving test. She panicked going over Cunningham's Gap – a windy, single lane road with national park on either side. The Gap cuts through the Great Dividing Range and into the west. There was a long row of trucks and cars backing up behind her as she putted along and took each bend like someone who has been driving for two months would, white-knuckling the steering wheel. They overtook aggressively as we emerged from the pass, honking and accelerating like maniacs.

'Shit, shit shit,' she said, terrified.

'It's all right. Take your time. Just calm down,' I spluttered.

'Stop yelling at me!'

'I'm not yelling!'

'Oh my god, Mum. You are not helping at all,' she muttered.

It's not been a relaxing trip.

I remember learning to drive in my cousin Vinod's 1983 Holden Gemini SL/X. It was faded cherry-maroon. The X was for luxury, but by 1997 the luxury had long gone. Vinny sat in the passenger seat, coaching me as I drove around the backyard at Bridge Street. 'Give it some juice. Bit more juice. Now eeeease off the clutch. Ease. You're not easing.' I was terrible at changing gears. I stalled constantly. The first time I ever swore in front of Fari was in that car. We were stuck at a stop sign, with a line-up of honking cars behind us. I just couldn't get it started. I would ease off the clutch, lurch an inch forward, then bunny-hop, rattle and stall. Mum was forever reminding us that the tongue we had been given to mention God should not be defiled with slander or bad language. In that sweaty panic, I do believe my exact turn of phrase was: 'Fuck, fuck. Jesus Christ. Fuck off. Oh my god. Fuck.'

Fari was so appalled at my outburst we had to pull over into a side street so that I could apologise. Which I did, and then muttered curses under my breath all the way home.

Borhan and the boys are on their way to meet us and take us out to the property. The boys have been living out here for a while now. They've been back to see me, but this is our first visit to their new home.

'Come on,' I say to Layla, pushing the car door shut. 'I'll buy you a Coke.'

We step into the pub and order two Cokes, and sit ourselves up at the front bar. We look around, and then at each other, and start to giggle.

'Literally where are we?' laughs Layla.

'I literally do not know,' I say.

She's looking at her phone. 'Three missed calls from Grandma.'

'Oh jeez.' I check my phone. 'I have two.'

'I'll call her now.'

It won't be urgent. It will be the drive. Mum doesn't like us driving.

Layla grabs her Coke and walks out the back of the pub to the beer garden, phone under her ear. She calls her grandmother every day. They talk when they are worried, or sad or anxious. They talk when they're happy and glad. In Persia they have a saying: Toh noor-e cheshm-e man haste – You are the light of my eyes. Fari is legally blind now. Macular degeneration has stolen the centre of her vision, but not the peripheries. Layla is the light of her eyes.

Leo and Borhan arrive at the pub. Leo bounds through the door and runs up to me, wrapping himself around my waist. I squeeze my youngest boy and kiss his whole head. Every bit of it. He smiles. 'Hi, Mumsy.'

'Hello, my baby,' I say, pulling back to look at him. Tanned, rosy-cheeked, dirt under his fingernails. My sunshine. He's wearing a necklace with a bull head on it, jeans, muddy farm boots, a hunting knife sheathed and strapped to his belt. Big eyes, big smile. He's all face, is our Leo.

'Where's your brother?' I ask.

'He'll meet us at the gate. He wants to drive you in himself,' Leo says, rolling his eyes. 'He thinks he's so good now he can drive.'

'I'm not getting in the car if Will is driving,' Layla says. Leo grins and throws himself on her. At last, an ally.

Borhan and I ignore them. We jump in the front seats of his ute and they get in the back with the dogs, whose tails are threatening to wag right off. I pretend to hate the hounds, but I pat them in secret and whisper in their ears that I will dip biscuits into my tea for them later. Rocky gives a regal sniff of acknowledgement. Sage plasters my ear with her wet tongue.

William meets us at the gate of the property. He's driving a beat-up once-white 1985 LandCruiser. He's named this paddock basher 'Swampy'. It has a king-sized bull bar and a weird rain water collection system in the tray. Will's wearing an enormous Akubra hat and his sleeves are rolled up. My thirteen-year-old son steps out of the truck looking like he's passed through a wormhole and become a man. Well, a man-ling. A baby-man. I'm emotional at the transformation. I hug him and for the first time, my arms feel small around his torso, and my nose is even with his. I kiss his cheeks and pull off his hat to see his whole face. 'Argh, gimme that . . .' he says, pulling it back on his head. 'You can't just take a man's hat, Mum!'

I get into the cab. The floor is rusted, the seat-cushion thin. I flip open the glove compartment and an empty Coke can falls out. Will starts the engine and eases smoothly into first, working the clutch and gearstick as easy as riding a bike. He accelerates with a whoosh. Showing off.

'Is this car safe, William?' I ask, clasping the armrest.

'Nah, but it's fast.' He grins.

The sun dips and we pass over a wide creek. The banks are winding and ragged, peppered with rocks, clumps of love grass and overhanging gums. The water is greeny-grey. Slow moving.

'The MacIntyre Brook,' Will says. 'It's about a kilometre to the shed from here.'

'Caught any fish in there?'

'Yeah, some. Catfish, perch, Murray cod. Went fishing with the neighbours.'

We pass through a hilly pasture of spear grass, dotted with patches of tiny purple and yellow wildflowers. The road turns sandy as we wind through a cypress pine wood. The wood opens up onto a grassy plain with solitary trees scattered about. Clusters of hop bush and rosemary, and a lone, silvery red-gum. Three kangaroos look up at the same time and follow us with their heads before bounding over the rocky pasture, towards the dam.

William is rough and he is tough, but underneath it all there is a different sort of mind at work. When he was eight years old he said to me, 'You know, Mum, the patterns you see in the sand of the desert have never been there before. They change every night because of the wind. They're like a fingerprint. Never the same twice. So, when you see the desert sand, you're seeing something original.'

In the months before Borhan took him to the bush, Will was suspended from school for fighting. He hates school. He's always hated it. But he loves to read. For years his primary school report card said 'William daydreams' and 'William needs to pay attention'. His sister was a model student. School captain. We couldn't understand why Will hated it so much. When I asked his teachers what he was doing instead of his class work, they said, 'He looks out the window a lot.' Now, he's driving like he's been doing it for years, chatting easily to me about soil and pig tracks and the wild camels. 'I'm gonna be a drover one day, Mum. And a bush mechanic,' he says. He is animated. I believe him.

We reach the stockyard and I see the shed. It's enormous, but it's still a shed. Borhan's driven up ahead and he's waiting there with the other two. Leo hops on his dirt bike and does some lappies around the shed so I can see him ride. The dogs run around, chasing swallows, bounding over blue-grass. It's all bronzed, outback goodness.

The inside of the shed is quite homely. Persian rugs cover the concrete floor, and the large space is divided into zones. There are beds and couches and a makeshift kitchen. Everything is solar-powered, but there's a generator in case of an emergency. Leo's been making my tea for years, and now he boils water over a gas burner and brews me up a strong cup, with milk and sugar. We watch the sun go down over the hills.

Night falls and brings a cold wind. Will chops some wood, Borhan and Leo make a fire together. Layla and I navigate the logistics of going to the loo when there isn't a loo. We heat up a lasagne in the barbecue and eat it around the fire. 'Come and see the night frogs, Mum,' says Leo, pulling me to the water tanks. I love frogs. There are hundreds of them. He squeals as I pick one up and offer it to him. It's cold and leathery-damp. The little suction pads feel tacky on my skin. Leo shows me the outdoor shower. It has a solar heater attached. 'A frog went in it, so it broke,' he says. 'Dad says we'll have to have cold showers until we get another one.' I decide to skip showering.

When the kids are asleep, Borhan and I sit out near the dying embers. A nightcap. The sky is cloudless. A fingernail moon. The Milky Way is just inches from the treetops, spread out like dropped diamonds.

'I'm writing a book,' I tell him. 'A publishing house wants to buy it.'

'Wow,' he says, genuinely. 'That's great, Seets. I always knew you would.'

'It's sort of a memoir. You're in it.'

'Oh, god!' He laughs. 'Every story needs a villain, I suppose . . .'

He throws his paper plate into the coals. It catches alight with an orange whoosh. A tawny frogmouth makes itself known in the rough-barked apple, nearby.

'There are no villains,' I say. 'It's a book about love.'

Today.

I ate some cheese and bread. I wrote. I drank sweet, milky tea. I kissed a man on his lips and shoulders. I made a sandwich for my daughter. I marked six short stories and a paper on Oscar Wilde. I walked two dogs that aren't mine. I called Ma. I bought red wine and slow-boiled a lamb-shank soup. I read the last two pages of a novel and closed the cover, unsatisfied. I pulled letters out of the mailbox. I paid the power bill. I ate a square of Turkish delight. I made love in the dark.

It was nothing, and it was everything.

When a child is raised with unshakeable faith, they are taught that the path they are on is the righteous path. They are shown all the choices and told which ones are the right ones to make and which ones lead them away from God. Why should they stray from the path and wander into the forest? Why should they choose to risk their virtue and their soul?

For me, having faith was an experience of developing great courage in someone else's convictions. When I began taking bits of God away, giving myself permission to be less certain and more curious, I realised I didn't have any convictions I was sure were my own, let alone any mistakes. Now, I have both.

And the forest is incredible. It's dark and deep, yes. But in other places it's dappled with light so beautiful and clearings so vast and strong it makes you weep to think you might have missed it. The forest teaches you that there is no order without chaos, and no liberation without bonds. That there is no forgiveness without error, no honesty without deceit, and no loyalty without betrayal. Courage does not exist if you do not feel fear, and joy is nothing unless you have known sorrow. In the forest of unbelieving, I can look without judgement or the prism of righteousness covering my eyes. My goodness belongs to me, and so does my corruption. As it does to us all. The story of vice and of virtue is the story of being human.

Steinbeck writes, 'There is one story in the world and only one . . . A man, after he has brushed off the dust and chips of his life will have only the hard, clean questions: was it good or was it evil. Have I done well – or ill?' It is not our God or our church or our scripture that gives us our humanity, but our ability to choose.

Whether this world is a fairground God designed to test us, or a random collection of rocks that landed in a particularly auspicious sector of the galaxy, we know that we are not here for long. Perhaps we are not meant for this place, its ruinous wars and shifting sands. Our molten sun is less violent than our earth. We could, any one of us at any minute, come to the end of it. And who knows what we will find.

Wherever you are in place, somewhere else a city is being destroyed. Somewhere else, a couple is sharing their first gaze at their baby. Somewhere, a mother is holding her dying son in her arms, and a father is walking his daughter down the aisle. Somewhere, there is a child who is stepping out in front of a car, and a driver who will never recover. Somewhere, a boy is putting his hands on a girl's breasts for the first time, and a girl is finding out what it means to be touched.

There is no such thing as hell, other than the terrible and ruthless hells we make for ourselves, and there is no such thing as heaven, except for those moments of heavenly sublimity that take us broken and spit us out whole again.

Our time here is ten thousand years of Sufi poetry versus one minute of carnal desire. It's seventeen years raising a child versus seven seconds in a rolling car. It's juicy, cut mangoes. It's stale bread. It's ginger in your tea. It's a saint praying to a god they've stopped believing in, while an atheist thumbs her rosary beads in the dark. It's a beggar eating oysters fresh from the sea, while a king eats old blood, twice fried in the stomach of a pig. It's a small thing, until it isn't, and it's a big thing, until it's not. And all of it comes around again and again, and again and again.

So let your fear sit nicely with its hands in its lap, and listen instead to the sounds of the women who raised you, from babe to bearer of the living.

Because there is nothing lost that cannot be found.

And whatever your question . . .

The answer is love.

AUTHOR'S NOTE

The factual events in this book have been poured through several sieves – fading memories, second hand accounts, and my own poetic imagination. Some minor characters are fictional, created from a wisp of memory, a line of dialogue, or simply a 'feeling' someone had about something that happened a very long time ago.

That said, most of this book is absolutely true.

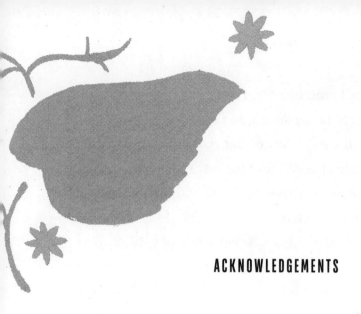

ACKNOWLEDGEMENTS

Many thanks:

To Brigid Mullane, my publishing editor, and the team at Ultimo Press, for taking a chance on an English teacher from Brissy, and showing me the ropes with kindness, generosity and effusive praise.

To my family, in particular: Shabnam, Vinny, Nabil, Sue and Nikita, for reading draft one and providing invaluable feedback in ways only cousins can.

To the Mansfield State High School English department, for coffee, cake and synonyms. In particular, to my heads of department, Carissa and Kevin, for their understanding and support.

To my students, for their youthful charm, and for railing against nihilism and electronic apathy in inspirational ways.

To my grandmother, for showing me the limitless power of unconditional love.

To my aunts, for being incomparable.

To my siblings, for being such good sports.

To Borhan, for his confidence that readers will read past page one, and his exceptional love for our children.

To my neighbours and friends in Tarragindi, for their comradeship and joie de vivre.

To Amelia, for being aggressively loyal since 1982. Best friends, forever.

To Anthony, for his excellent conversation and remarkable wit. If I was affected enough to claim a muse, you would be it, sweetheart.

To my parents, who love me anyway.

and

To my children, who bring it all home with grand esprit de corps. Never change, my darlings.

Sita Walker is an English and Literature high school teacher in Brisbane. Her first piece, 'Love in the Time of Grandmother', was shortlisted in the SBS Emerging Writers Competition and was published by Hardie Grant in the anthology, *Roots: Home is Who We Are*. Before that, she dabbled in blogging and wrote short letters to her students. *The God of No Good* is her debut book.